D1062529

I Ain't Marchin' Anymore!

I Ain't Marchin' Anymore!*

By Dotson Rader

* from the song, I AIN'T MARCHIN' ANYMORE
by Phil Ochs © 1964 by Appleseed Music Inc., all rights reserved

DAVID McKAY COMPANY, Inc.   **New York**

I AIN'T MARCHIN' ANYMORE!

COPYRIGHT © 1969 BY DOTSON RADER

All rights reserved, including the right to reproduce
this book, or parts thereof, in any form, except for
the inclusion of brief quotations in a review.

HQ
799.7
.R 33

Library of Congress Catalog Card Number: 76-79507

MANUFACTURED IN THE UNITED STATES OF AMERICA

VAN REES PRESS • NEW YORK

dedication

With thanks to my teachers—Daniel B. Dodson, Lionel Trilling, William A. Owens—for their encouragement and help.

Praise to my friends in the Movement for their courage.

For John Conrad Weiser.

ALMA COLLEGE
MONTEITH LIBRARY
ALMA, MICHIGAN

In 1962 SEVENTY-FIVE STUDENT LEADERS WERE IN-
vited by the Student League For Industrial Democracy to
form the first national convention of a new student organization: Students For A Democratic Society (SDS). The delegates met for a week at a labor-owned camp in Port Huron,
Michigan, and produced a statement whose first and final
drafts were written by a former University of Michigan *Daily*
editor turned activist, Tom Hayden. The Port Huron Statement, as it was called, established the ideological basis for
SDS and became a basic document of the New Left. This
statement reads in part:

"WE ARE PEOPLE of this generation, bred in at least
modest comfort, housed in universities, looking uncomfortably to the world we inherit.... Our work is guided by the
sense that we may be the last generation in the experiment
with living....

"ANY NEW LEFT in America must be, in large measure,
a Left with real intellectual skills.... The university permits
the political life to be an adjunct to the academic one, and
action to be informed by reason.

"A NEW LEFT must be distributed in significant social

vii

roles throughout the country. The universities are distributed in such a manner.

"A NEW LEFT must consist of younger people who matured in the post-war world, and must be directed to the recruitment of younger people. The university is an obvious beginning point.

"A NEW LEFT must start controversy across the land, if national policies and national apathy are to be reversed. The ideal university is a community of controversy, within itself and in its effects on communities beyond.

"A NEW LEFT must transform modern complexity into issues that can be understood and felt close-up by every human being. It must give form to the feelings of helplessness and indifference, so that people may see the political, social and economic sources of their private troubles and organize to change society. The case for change, for alternatives that will involve uncomfortable personal efforts, must be argued as never before. The university is a relevant place for all these activities. . . .

"To turn these possibilities into realities will involve national efforts at university reform by an alliance of students and faculty. They must wrest control of the educational process from the administrative bureaucracy. . . . They must import major public issues into the curriculum. . . . They must make debate and controversy . . . the common style for educational life. They must consciously build a base for their assault upon the logic of power."

It was not until 1965 that Students For A Democratic Society came to national prominence. It was in the second half of this decade that campus-based rebellion, coupled with the militancy of the disaffected off-campus, became the primary channel for resistance to American imperialism and racism and began the movement toward a second American revolution.

I Ain't Marchin' Anymore!

chapter one

"AMERICA," RACHEL SAID, "AMERICA WAS GOING TO be so different. Everybody who ever came here, even before the country was really alive, everybody thought America would be so different from the place they left. It was going to be so good." We were sitting in an afterhours bar on lower Broadway. It was five in the morning and the dawn was opening outside. Everyone was tired. Street hustlers who had made no score and were hungry, junkies about to come down, and kids—New York, the East Village especially, was always full of Dickensian Flower Children away from home permanently (written in crayon inside the bandshell in Tompkins Park: Call me home, Ma, sometime call me home), and five or six of the Brotherhood sitting in the back waiting for the nod of the Mafia-captain to do what it is men in the Organization do at five in the morning, squinting repulsively at the Miss Bessie queens who flitted in thrift-shop drag in the semi-darkness trying to catch, for a moment, the male hunger in the male eye and, in the glance, to be *women* at last, authentically *femme*, for once in their poor lives.

Rachel The Social Worker was tired from pandering after the good will of black parents (usually only the mother admitted paternity) in the hope of breaking the poverty cycle and giving the kids a chance to find America outside the filth of the Lower East Side (which was, I can assure you, a far better slum than Harlem, better far than East Harlem, far, far better than Bedford-Stuyvesant). Rachel then was one of the last of her kind, a young, non-violent revolutionary, crusted with cynicism, her sensitivity worn by daily facing the hopelessness of her job (she worked with the poor in block organizing, fought to improve the schools, watched out for the sick, played Little Miss City Hall to the wretched of the Lower East Side) yet beneath it all, running deep, she shared with me the memory of the promise of making America come true before the riots and the war. And she clung to it. She loved America, or rather she loved what she had once imagined America to be. She knew better now, as I did, but still, like a kind of invidious, ineluctable nostalgia, she kept faith, in the heart, with what America was to be. She did not believe it possible of birth, but she worked at its labor—forever in labor, forever in pain.

Rachel was a revolutionary, before every youth with long hair and anger took the title, and she acted in the name of the *promise* of America; come hell or high water, she would kill herself before she would let America settle irreclaimably in the injustice and stupor of the middle class, before she would give it over finally to the pigs and gangsters and generals and preachers and politicians and businessmen and liberal educational managers who had committed the theft of its spirit before it came of birth.

"America isn't *really* America, if you know what I mean," she said, looking up at me, speaking her hope, sipping the beer which had cost me a buck, most of it to pay off the local police. "And it won't be until every ghetto, the whole damn place is pure again, as clean as it was before Americans ruined it."

Before Americans ruined it. Americans. And I wondered what terrible venality, what poverty of the spirit, greed, wittlessness, what lust for dissolution made my country so violent

2

and ugly and depraved and smug. For it was all these things. It *was* to have been such a different place. That is what we loved about it. Its former promise. But then I was going to be so different, too. I was going to try to make the world a better place to live. Excuse the dated sentiment, but I was going to try to make it a better place. And sitting with Rachel in the bar, the queens screeching like frightened birds in the back in the smoke, the hustlers slouching manfully against the bar, a meat rack without buyers, holding a beer or cigarette butch in their hands, trying to look cold and indifferent while inside I knew them to be frightened of the morning without a score's bread to take them through to night, and the junkies holding tight, off on their own terrible trip fearing a fall, and the petty Organization goons, like off-duty cops, sitting at their table believing they were feeding on us while, in fact, we were each exploited by the nation, aliens inside, in refuge in a bar afterhours waiting for fatigue or boredom or disgust to take us home to wake to what in the afternoon?

I was at Columbia. I had classes to attend and profs to impress and beyond that, serving as an end, the protection of my friends and their comfort of me. I sought to protect them in part by political activism, not the rigidly non-violent kind, that was killed in 1964 with the Great Civil Rights Bill that brought a decade of peaceful protest to a close and accomplished nothing else, but political activism that worked to create confrontation with agencies of the System and allowed us, if not to win, at least to physically choose against a society and a war we abhorred.

Rachel? She had a dirty room without a private toilet and lights that did not work half the time and neighbors whose coughs could be heard through the walls. And friends chosen by a wider, more compassionate standard than mine.

"You know, Dotson, I never even knew a black person until I was fifteen. They were in school and everything, but

I never knew one until then. And when I first got to know one . . . he wasn't all that great . . . all I wanted was to be fucked by him." She laughed, embarrassed. "I suppose to make up for lost time." She paused and glanced at me to see how I would take it. Rachel I loved and she knew I suspected she went to bed with blacks and she knew I hated the idea and I hated hating it. "Unloaded a lot of guilt when it happened. And it wasn't until I had done it and seen how ordinary it was, not until then could I love them. That's when they became people to me."

I do not remember even *seeing* a real, live black man in the flesh, personally, up close, until I was fourteen. Rachel had them in school, but I never did, nor in the neighborhoods where I was raised, nor in the churches (most especially *not* in the churches). Except for seeing them as menials in Hollywood movies (Stepin Fetchit, bug-eyed, cretinistic, hysteric, seeing ghosts and hearing ghostly noises and reporting them to the super-cool Mr. Chan; Prissy/Butterfly McQueen, lazy, incompetent, driving poor Mistress Scarlett up the goddamn wall: "But I's couldn't find da doctah, Miz Scarlett!") the fullest education I received about blacks came from missionary slides and films at church missionary conferences where they were shown nude, the women full and low-breasted, the children lugging large, distended bellies on their tiny frames, the men half-naked, befeathered, fierce, paddling down the Niger to the Mission Compound. Let Us Take Up The White Man's Burden. My early attitude toward the black was formed by the missionary doctrine of bringing the White Man's Gospel, medicine and technology to the Sons of Ham, spreading the machines and techniques and the attitudes that lay waste to the earth. The missionary view of the blacks held me until school when the legend of Lincoln took its place. That (the embracing of Abe Lincoln by the heart) was a first step in Americanization, for it was the All-American myth of a man least like us whom we believed to be ourselves. Lincoln, secretly held, and the Mississippi River were two forces in my childhood central to the formation of my concern.

I have always been interested in what it means to be an American, what there is about the American character that differentiates it from other national types. Beyond our violence and greed and incredible national hypocrisy, what there is about us that enables us to produce children capable of the sacrifice and rage Rachel evidenced. I do not know, but in my mind Lincoln and the River touch upon the contradictions, the violence and the goodness, fading, debilitated, of America.

My family once lived on the Mississippi bluffs. As a kid I played on the banks and sandbars of the river and in winter I ran on the ice and I used to think about Tom Sawyer and Huck Finn scheming against Aunt Polly along the river and about Abe Lincoln as a boy floating a raft down the Mississippi and inadvertently seeing a slave auction, that one base exhibition drawing his conscience against slavery.

When I did meet a black man for the first time—he was from Ghana (a country which was the liberal rage of the Fifties) and he spoke in what I assumed was an Oxford accent —the experience was upsetting, considering what I had been told about their natural rhythm and smell, their need of Mission training, their animalism and stupidity. At the time I wanted very badly to reach out and touch his woolly hair, to smell his skin, to see him nude, to see if what I had heard was true. What I learned from meeting him was that blacks were as intelligent, as gentle, as *human* as whites (and for a Midwestern kid this was a new understanding). Despite the recognition of equality there remained to the black an aura of mystery. They were like me, yet they were different, unknown, coming from a state and culture other than mine. I found them fascinating.

5

One fall I was jumped by four black high school students as I walked, after a night football game, from the stadium to the bus stop. I was grabbed by the youths and pulled behind some bushes, roughed up a bit and ordered to shine one of the boy's shoes. I was about their age. I was scared pissless. The boy with the unshined shoes put his foot on a large rock, crossed his arms over his chest and stood like an Indian chief scanning the horizon, his eyes looking beyond me.

"Shine them shoes," he said in an even voice, as if he were ordering a meal.

"With what?" I asked, ready to do the work, given the tools.

"Ya got a snot rag?"

Down I went before the rock and spit on his shoes and polished away. As I worked, the blacks made jokes about how humiliated the white boy must feel. That was all there was to it.

When it was over I was disappointed, for I had expected violence. I thought the living shit would be knocked out of me in the bushes by the blacks. I both feared and wanted it to happen, wanted violence that tested a man, brought into the open the ambivalency of feeling I held toward this other race which occupied the continent with us (whites). It was like a bad marriage where, as Lionel Trilling has noted, the very things which make it unbearable also make it unbreakable. I was about fifteen and I suspected that part of the significance of the black in the white imagination was the potential of their violence. And violence was liberating.

In 1956 Hungary came along. I listened to the reports of the fighting in Budapest on the radio. I saw newsreels about the Freedom Fighters defying Russian tanks in the streets (corroded by the outrage it elicited in my mind the picture of a young Hungarian student with a brick in his hand standing bravely before a Russian tank moments before his death) and I was angry at America's refusal to go to the aid of the Hungarians. I was ashamed of my country and disgusted with our platitudes and moralistic posturing.

That is when I think it began. The disaffection from America. The suspicion of her motives. The disbelief in her essential decency.

I came from a religious home. My great-aunt was a medical missionary who had the misfortune of being captured by the Japanese and interned with Dutch plantation owners for the duration of the war. Out of the ten thousand or so imprisoned in the Sumatran camp only a few hundred survived the torture and the war. My aunt was among them.

By the time I entered college I disbelieved the faith my great-aunt had suffered confinement for, but remaining of it, still gripping my imagination, was the conviction that Evil—repression, hunger, ignorance, plague, violence—was in the world and that good and just men acted in opposition to it; and that the greatest love was the willingness to give one's life for one's friends.

My family came to America in 1643. To each generation, like some hereditary disease, was transferred the sense of proprietorship over the land, the conviction that personal destiny was woven into the destiny of the American race, that I, as a member of a family that had survived the land, was responsible for the land. When my religious faith petered out—that is how it went, quickly dribbling away—my faith in the Dream of the country grew. America-To-Come became vital. Without any goddamn Foursquare City to prepare for, with no Second Coming to establish the City of God, I had to work to end the mess. I was responsible.

After Hungary I did not really like America as it was (I did not really like God, either). The question was how did one make America into its promise. For those of us who were young in the early Sixties the way we discovered was the Civil

Rights and Peace Movements. Many of us (like Tom Hayden, co-founder of SDS, raised in a Catholic home) were believers without a faith in need of Mission. Only that—the assurance of Mission—provided meaning.

In the early Sixties we in the student Left believed that our dissent from American capitalism had to be expressed within the limits of democratic practice. Part of this came from a belief in Martin Luther King's theories of non-violence. We had faith in the System's responsiveness to democratic appeal. It took incredible failure for us to abandon pacific protest. It took the urban riots and the Vietnam war. Our demand was that the American Dream be realized. And it was this demand —that a national abstraction be actualized—which made us quintessentially American. Rachel working through her slums was building on that Dream, and it was something that pre-dated our disaffection, that came before us and before the land. It was what set the American character apart, gave it its distinctive pride and its growing sense of failure before its own hope.

Rachel and I left the afterhours bar about six in the morning. We walked across Bleecker to Sixth Avenue and up Twelfth Street. It was a weekend morning, cool, the streets were empty except for an occasional wino sleeping off a drunk, a few fags coming home from the baths and parties and trick's beds, and the trash examiners rifling the litter baskets on the street. At Bleecker we turned up Thompson and walked through Washington Square. The sun was clouded by pollution-haze and the light, gray, made the Arch seem particularly definite, bright and beautiful, its stone seeming ancient and very tactile near the trees. Before we walked over to Sixth Avenue we sat on a park bench and smoked a ciga-rette. The fountain in the center of the Square was off, but a puddle of water remained in its bowl and pigeons strutted around it, bowing to sip as we watched. It felt good sitting by her, my arm around her small shoulders, her head bent, her hair long and brown and falling over her head, shielding her eyes from me. We were worn out. Sunday and tomorrow, after the day with me, she would go back to Avenues A and B and the neighborhood and the violence.

There was something about Rachel that was ineffably delicate, not simply her despair, which was growing, but her body and manners, fragile, doll-like, incapable of survival.

As we sat together quietly, three black kids came running into the park laughing. They raced up the promenade and into the area by the fountain where we were sitting. They stopped running when they noticed us. They huddled together. They grew wary. Rachel smiled at them. They ran by us and, as they did, one of the boys veered near Rachel and grabbed the scarf she held in her hands and ran off with it. I moved to go after them and she stopped me with her hand.

"You little thieving bastards!" I shouted.

"What's a scarf?" she asked, laughing at my anger.

"It isn't the scarf," I said, sounding like my father. "It's the principle of the thing."

"What principle? They haven't anything pretty. They want a pretty scarf."

I was going to reply that they should buy one, then, but I did not since she would only retort: with what?

I was offended by the theft, not because of the value of the scarf, but because my self-image had been offended by the act. We were no ordinary honkies, we were two people on *their* side, friends, we worked for them, before they were in school, and we still did. They were stealing from their friends. It wasn't right.

Rachel looked up at me, still smiling. "Baby," she said, her voice gay, "you take everything so personal. They didn't see us. They only saw the scarf." But that was the offense. They did not see us, not as we were defined by our past. They only saw the scarf.

Summer. 1961. The Kennedy Years. Fifteen of us met at night in Dupont Circle in Washington. We were all in our late teens or early twenties and we were tired from having spent the day sitting-in against segregation at a diner in Maryland. We gathered around the fountain in the park, feeling strong and morally upright and optimistic about America, believing justice was a matter of forcing white men to sell black men Coca-Colas and apartments and good jobs and good education throughout the South. The task was simple. The North would convert the South.

It was hot that night and the air smelled of our sweat. We sang "We Shall Overcome," loudly, proudly. We talked up our triumph.

Our triumph. The owner closed the diner four hours early and sent the waitress home. (The Southern waitress: rural, bone-tired, feet pained, racially arrogant, thinking herself the Prize raging the black man's hunger; in a yellow hairnet and soiled uniform, drinking endless Doctor Peppers in great gulps before thirsty Northern integrationists.) We stayed inside after closing time, sitting on hard stools, the lights out, the owner coming from the back room every few minutes to give out with increasingly desperate, plaintive orders that we leave. "Goin' call the *poh*lice if y'all don't git. Y'hear? Goin' git me some hep from the 'thorities ... y'all git the hell otta heah!" Yankee troublemakers. We sat staring ahead at the mirror behind the shelves of danish and doughnuts. And then our leader started singing, *black and white together we shall not be moved ... just like a tree planted by the water we shall not be moved.* Singing it out, my throat tightening with the sense of unexpected courage, the image of rural Southern ambushes and police thugs vivid in my mind, all the years of wanting to act in unavoidable risk on behalf of the unfree, and there I sat like a picture out of *The New York Times*, playing *Northern Integrationist Liberal* to the hilt, really believing (and that was what was different then) that a sit-in against segregation *meant* something. In my mind applauding my moral purity, feeling a sense of solidarity with the blacks sitting beside me, a solidarity with the entire black nation.

I did not know why I had come. But my sitting-in, as other college students had and would sit-in until 1964 when Watts brought the Southern summer to a close, grew out of white guilt (what else?) and an attempt to declare the gap between our generation and our parents'. That assertion of moral and historical uniqueness by my generation characterized the period of youth revolt inaugurated by the Freedom Riders.

The owner left the diner. For an hour I sat with the others waiting for the cops. For the press. For the Northern lawyer to come and spring us. God, were we smug and self-righteous. No wonder the crackers hated us.

The owner returned alone. In the half light he went over to the Coke machine (a symbol of equality to Freedom Riders, heaven being the place where anyone may order a Coke) and poured out a soda for each of us, black and white. A lanky man, wiry, nervous, with long, thin hands fidgeting with the counter cloth as he watched us slowly sip our triumph. An American businessman, hung on profit and loss, wondering what the hell fifteen Cokes would cost him when the neighbors learned. We had won the game. But it didn't mean a damn.

1966. Sunday morning in the fall, walking with Rachel in the Village, taking her to Twelfth Street where I hoped to make love to her in the afternoon, or failing that—I thought my chances were narrowing as the conversation became more political—just to hold her for awhile.

"I don't see what the hell we can do in this country, short of open revolution, I don't see where we can make any progress short of that," she said, her politics being desperate. "Some kind of revolution's the only way out."

"No, babe," I said, waxing moderate, "you know what happened in Harlem and Watts when the riots broke. It never'll work. Not in the United States." That I believed, just as I believed nothing else would work either. During the 1962 Cuban Missile Crisis—we were all Jack's children then—I was in the pacifistic, democratic Leftist Student Peace Union (there was no SDS at the time; the Castroite Fair Play For Cuba Committee, which went underground that year, was the closest thing to revolutionary on campus) and we picketed and rallied against Kennedy and the Russians and, at the same time (we were two-issue people), we picketed Woolworth's protesting segregation in their Southern outlets. It did not do one goddamn bit of good. But what else was there? Playing jungle rebels in Harlem?

"I don't know, Honey," she said, walking along beside me, her arm in mine. "I know I can't go on like this. I can't take this shit no more. Liberal wars. Liberal welfare. Liberal slums. People are *dying*, Honey, in America. The System has to be changed."

But how? SDS was in existence at Columbia, although it was very weak, and Tom Hayden and Mario Savio had visited the campus in 1964 and they had talked about Berkeley and talked about "participatory democracy" and the use of "confrontation politics" and the techniques of disruption to force the System to reveal the repressive nature of its power and intent, but I did not think that would work. I believed America to be racist—every ghetto in America testified to that—and imperialist and a very real threat to the lives of my friends (the SSS draft was picking them off) yet I did not know how to resist the System. I, like every other young Leftist, was powerless. We were disregarded, not only politically, but educationally. The university disregarded our opinion, as did every other "adult, liberal" institution. And most pathetically we had no say whatever in what use the government would make of our lives. Lewis Hershey could pack us off to his bloody patriotic wars and kill us off and we could do nothing about it.

"I used to think," Rachel said, "that by organizing the poor you could move to changing the System. I don't believe it no more. I don't think what I do does a damn thing . . . Honey, like last week, Maria R——'s kid got bit by a rat, once in the chest and once on the thigh, you know, it was awful and she wouldn't take the baby to the hospital because she can't speak English and she's frightened of the welfare bureaucrats and the doctors and she thinks the hospital's a butcher shop, which it is, and the kid's going to die if he doesn't get some help. Now get this, I take the kid to a private doctor and I tell him about him and the doctor sort of fixes him up and he sends me a bill, like a hundred dollars, he sends me a bill for fixing a baby up and I tell him I don't have money and she don't have money and he says pay up before you bring the little bastard back for a recheck he needs. American doctors. Great. Corrupt as hell, like everything else in this sweet land of ours . . . and now two more PR boys, thirteen years old, are hooked on junk and nobody gives a shit . . . a murder a week or more, the poor killing the poor, shit, it goes on and on and on and, Dotson, you come over here in the West Village, so much goddamn wealth and uptown even more, billions, Rockefeller and the rest, and a few blocks south of them and north of them, just a few blocks from them fat cats, people are dying and nobody gives a damn and kids, younger than us, Honey, are dying everyday in Johnson's war, *their* liberal war, not just the poor bastard soldier, not just those young, young guys, but peasants and peasants' kids, civilians . . . and they're dying from our weapons in other places on the earth and nobody gives a good shit . . . Honey," she said, squeezing my arm tightly, "Honey, revolution's got to come, baby, it's *got* to come."

And for the first time, walking with her, for the first time I, too, wanted revolution . . . in my gut, there, inside like part of me, inside true, I wanted it to come, wanted the senseless, everlasting killing, the goddamn misery, the poverty to end. Wanted *justice*. Wanted to make the fat cats pay, baby, *pay* for disregarding the anguish of their weaker, poorer countrymen. And the hope still there, under the thirst for blood, the Dream that out of it would come America clean and just and, Christ, so goddamn much better than before.

I held her in bed. I kissed her and tried to arouse her but she was so tired and wanted sleep. When she was asleep I got out of bed and turned on the light in the closet and the light in the closet fell on the bed and softly lighted her face and brown hair spread on the white pillow catching the light and the closed eyes, the little face, her lovely face.

About a month later I saw her at the West End Bar, a saloon across from Columbia that was a center for radical students and former students and heads and old people from the SRO neighborhood who haven't any money and come and sit at booths with a glass of water and a napkin in front of them, sit for hours silently watching the students in the bar, looking out the window. It was in the late afternoon and the weather was getting colder. Rachel was sitting at a booth talking to Philip, a frat boy from a cake-eater family, and they were talking about how the New Left was trying to construct a new constituency out of the disaffected students, the black militants and the poor since the old Left—the Communists and Fellow Travelers (a joke), organized labor (sell-out), and the Leftist intellectuals (turned yellow and fat and middle-aged)—had been bought off. They talked about how Watts had turned the black youth from Martin King's Uncle Tom-ism to militancy and how the Vietnam war was having the

14

same effect on the disaffected young whites. Philip talked about CORE on campus and about what a bust their attempt at unionizing the University Food Service's colored employees had been.

As they talked I sat across from Rachel and watched her. She looked bad, not only weak and very tired, but her eyes seemed unusually large, her manner depressed. Philip talked on, defending American democracy, and when he would pause Rachel would say, "You don't understand. Non-violence won't work. Until you try to use non-violent protest to save lives and then lives die, until then...."

On Philip talked about the necessity of keeping dissent democratic, refusing to admit to Rachel's objection that it was meaningless since America was not a democracy and that playing by "democratic rules" was to play in a game where the rules were made by your opponent, a game you could never win. "Why do they have the right to use violence to maintain the System and we not have the right to use violence to change it?" And: "I think," she said, tiring of the argument, "that the only legitimate criteria is effectiveness."

That surprised me, for it struck me as ethical nihilism, for it could justify anything.

After awhile she left, taking the subway downtown to her friends. Several times Philip went down to see her and she tried to convert him to her revolutionary faith, tried to make him concede to responsibility for the desperation of the poor. Philip, while I think he loved Rachel—she was tiny and delicate, soft-spoken, and she had about her a sense of brokenness and lingering sadness which drew from one the desire to hold and protect her—could not bring himself to understanding or commitment. Several times he saw her, each time arguing with her, refusing to be convinced. Unconsciously disaffected himself, yet he could not accept the futility of working within "democratic" structures to bring reform. For to do so would be to choose against his family and his past and his conception of his countrymen. That he could not do.

It may be sentimental, but the image which remains most vivid in my mind about Rachel is the sight of her in the summer in the rain in Tompkins Park carrying a large red umbrella and having six small black children cling to her legs and dress as she walked shielding them through the rain. Much of the poignancy of that image is the remorse it calls forth. Knowing the positive, revolutionary direction her outrage took, I think of years I spent in the Civil Rights and Peace Movements playing by Liberal Establishment rules while the poor walked unshielded. My effort was meaningless.

The meaninglessness of non-violent, "democratic" methods was becoming clear to us in the spring of 1967. The Civil Rights Movement was dead. Pacifism was dead. Some Leftists —the Trotskyites, Maoists, radical socialists, anarchists, some of the radicals in SDS, Stokeley Carmichael, Rap Brown, Tom Hayden—knew it early. But it took the rest of us awhile to give up the sweet life of the democratic Left for revolt. Martin King and Roy Wilkins and Gus Hall and Hubert Humphrey never could give up the old patterns. But they are all dead now.

King tried in 1967, really tried to move beyond his age, to transcend his Baptist preacher-boy past and his unadmitted awe of White Life to unite the Civil Rights and anti-war movements in one mighty gesture and by it move Left to join the young and future with the militants. It did not work. He died before his death and he did not know it.

King made his grand gesture before the United Nations (another dead, liberal symbol) and while he shouted *End The War!* the New York police were introducing us to the war at home. We had come of age.

chapter two

APRIL 15, 1967. MORNING. THREE HUNDRED THOU-
sand people crowded the Sheep Meadow in Central Park,
spilled far north under the trees, from Fifth Avenue to Central
Park West, south from Columbus Circle to the Plaza. And
still they came.

Around ten o'clock I walked up Central Park West through
the heavy crowds along the stone hedges of the park where at
night homosexuals cruise in hunger trying to flag a trick to go
up the old dirt road. I had come to march in an anti-Vietnam-
war parade down Madison Avenue to the United Nations
where King and Carmichael would preach and William Buckley would take notes and the majority of us would return
home feeling good with the knowledge that we had done our
thing for peace. The parade was sponsored by the Spring
Mobilization To End The War In Vietnam, a coalition of
anti-war groups that spread ideologically from Dr. King's
Southern Christian Leadership Conference to the Trotskyist
Young Socialist Alliance, Progressive Labor Party and the
dowdy but still breathing—on F.B.I. dues—Communist Party,
U.S.A. It was the first attempt at a popular front since the
Thirties.

The corporate liberals, remembering Joe McCarthy and
thinking about their jobs and two-car-garage houses and chil-

dren in private schools, stayed clear of the whole thing, satis-
fied to liberally sniff that it was suspect to associate with Reds,
if not downright dangerous, and that, anyway, being liberal,
responsible war critics opposed the *escalation* of the conflict in
a better, more responsible, in short, a safer way: working within the System to influence the government toward more peaceful attitudes.

The Communists, too, were not pleased with the coalition
because it made apparent their moderation. They had grown
comfortable in the passing years, grown old and tired and
dated. It took great effort to revise your thinking.

The Communists, like the liberals, had learned nothing
since the Thirties. Now the workers had much more to lose
than their chains. The victim had become the executioner.
American labor supported the war. Enthusiastically.

It was a gray, cool day. Like New York generally in spring,
the park had a tired, dirty quality to it. That morning Central
Park West was clean of fags and the peace people cruised
there instead, trying to locate meeting points, working their
way into the line of march. Buses from New England and the
Midwest were parked along the side streets and avenues—
Harvard CORE, University of Wisconsin Young Democrats
—and pitchmen worked the crowd selling peace buttons and
American flags. A boy carried a sign: WAR IS GOOD BUSI-
NESS, INVEST YOUR SON.

I entered the park at 72nd Street. I wore an old tweed jacket
and tie and brown corduroy pants. I spent an hour trying to
find the area where the Columbia University contingent was
to assemble. That contingent would represent SDS (which
had no official representative on the Mobilization committee
because it thought that marches were a waste of time. It
organized draft card burning in the park instead) and other
student groups opposed to the Johnson-Humphrey war. We
were there to "witness" our outrage against the injustice of
our nation's foreign policy, to demonstrate that a majority

18

of concerned Americans wanted an immediate end to the war. It was to be a non-violent protest, an attempt to take that futile constitutional right—the right to petition for a redress of grievances—seriously.

Near 72nd Street I saw Philip, blond, tall, blandly good-looking, standing with a group of fraternity brothers listening to an old Socialist on the stand rail against capitalist wars. Philip stood with his hands on his hips, cool, listening with interest to the harangue, a slight smile, faintly superior and smug, on his lips. I greeted him.

"Goddamn, it's good to see you," he said, shaking my hand and introducing me to several of his friends, equally cool, faintly superior. I had not seen Philip in several months, not since he came to a party at my apartment and stayed late listening fascinated to an incredibly poor, disconsolate Tiny Tim sing (possessed by Ruth Etting that night, and the early Doris Day and once, accent and all, by Bessie Smith) of ten-cent dances and faded mean-to-me lovers and downhearted blues, babbling pretty Jesus child and love for the whole world and, you are *too* dear, thank you very much, oh thank you, of his endless rise to nowhere, the sainted chic freak arrested in time in time coming into his own ... Philip beguiled by disbelief, so convinced of his proprietorship—his place in the social and economic order—that at nineteen he was able to look upon the antics of his Leftist peers with an air of bemused tolerance. Philip, like upper-class WASPs in general, felt always sure of his ground. I thought too sure.

I asked him if he had seen any of the fellows around.

"I haven't been looking. To tell the truth I've been watching the rabble rouser." He indicated the old Socialist—bald, short, fat, sweating on that cool day, his collar open and pulled over the lapels of his jacket, speaking in the angry accents of Rachel's Lower East Side poor—cursing American capitalism on the stand and shaking his fist at the cake-eaters' pads on Fifth Avenue. "I thought fanatics like that went out with breadlines and apple peddlers," Philip commented, lighting a cigarette, holding it delicately between two fingers and striking the pose of the Main Liner slumming.

"They're back in style," I said, thinking what a piss-elegant son of a bitch thing for him to say. I was not a Socialist, but Philip made me defensive about anything on the Left. With him I could bring myself to defend the Stalinist purges and God knows what else.

"They're in vogue again? Really?" Philip asked incredulously, "I hope not. The Depression was thirty years ago. Times have changed, in case you hadn't noticed. The trouble with Reds," he said, mouthing a line he probably picked up at his father's club, "is that they can't stand prosperity." It sounded weak.

I let the fiction pass unchallenged. Like most of the moderate Company Students—those who if left unconverted by experience, in the following year, supported the university administration against the radical students—Philip believed that America was a decent country populated by free men in pursuit of the common good. He believed in American decency because he believed himself to be decent and good. And because his future lay unbounded before him he could not believe the actuality of *millions* of Americans without a future who existed in wretchedness and poverty. Maybe being from Haverford does that to you—for I had gone through Harlem with Philip and we had bought Puerto Rican whores in Chelsea and with him I had walked through the ghettos of New York and he had come out of it only to speak his fear of nonwhite violence and to say that there was an urgent need for better police work. Moderate. Liberal. Unable finally to believe, he found the propaganda of the Left to be ridiculous.

With that Philip and I strolled out of the Sheep Meadow, walking up the bridle path through a crowd of students from City College carrying placards—KILLING MORE, ENJOYING IT LESS? I DON'T GIVE A DAMN FOR UNCLE

20

SAM!—and middle-aged couples with small American flags and balloons and lunch bags.

As we walked I glanced through the trees over the crowded Sheep Meadow to the south to a small knoll and a tree where young men would burn their draft cards that afternoon— huddled in a circle, surrounded by supporters locking arms, kneeling away from the wind to deny the national purpose, placing their futures in default as they lit their cards with cigarette lighters and dropped the burning pieces into a coffee can held high above the group by a long-haired member of SDS. Over a hundred white cards would be burned, one of them owned by Gary Rader, twenty-three years old, who, after a year and a half of active service, would put on his Special Services Reserve uniform and travel from Chicago to New York to oppose the military more than the war. A Green Beret, no longer able to be simply another unthinking man following orders, through guilt he acted to repudiate his past, choosing against what was *unlike* him to become what he was. He could lie no more, take no more shit, bend no more to imperialism, whether American or Russian, no more be trained or train others to kill. He had had enough. It would cost him his freedom.

East, fluttering in the wind, were black anarchist flags and red flags and the starred flags of the National Liberation Front (Vietcong). From the north a contingent of Columbia University faculty came into the staging area wearing blue and red and black academic caps and gowns, walking slowly, self-consciously, their expressions rather too serious and self-regarding. One of them carried a small placard: CHILDREN ARE NOT BORN TO BURN. The parade had begun to move out pushing its way down Madison Avenue, six trucks filled with entertainers playing to curbside crowds, flowers, banners, leaflets falling, additional peace people continuing to jam the Meadow in such numbers that by the time the

21

speeches were over at the United Nations the last section of the parade was still waiting to leave the park.

There were advocates of war present, too. At Columbus Circle two American Legion members paced around the column, pausing now and again to guzzle beer, shouting, "Bomb Hanoi and Haiphong." The Peter Fechter Brigade (an ultra-Rightist bund named after a heroic East German youth murdered escaping over the Wall) shouted obscenities at the marchers on 45th Street and handed out leaflets demanding an invasion of North Vietnam. At 47th Street and Lexington Avenue workmen building the American Tobacco Company tower threw wet concrete and white paint at the demonstrators, shouting down from the safety of their scaffolding, "Red fuckers! Bomb Hanoi!" The police made no arrests. At Madison Avenue and 58th Street the everpopular American Nazi Party assembled in force and the four Storm Troopers jeered, "Who needs niggers?"

But the majority of the crowd was peaceful, ambling in the coolness of the day toward the United Nations, hoping the event would progress without incident, believing it already to be a success. As I looked over the great throng I felt proud of the Left, of its solidarity that day; I had a sense of excitement that comes with the conviction of being right and with the hope of winning. Perhaps, I thought, we *can* end the war through peaceful protest, perhaps the troops will come home when the government understands how profound the opposition is to the Vietnam war. And Philip, too, was evidence of probable victory for if the anti-war movement could attract political moderates and apolitical students into the cause, if people as basically indifferent to political activism as Philip could feel unease over the war—or at least over the threat of the draft to their future—then it seemed that there was real hope that the war might end soon. That day the majority of those present maintained faith in the efficacy of peaceful demonstration. They believed they could effect a reversal of

22

national policy through democratic means. But then they did not know how vitally important the war was to Lyndon Johnson. They did not know that faced with the choice of giving up the Presidency or ending the war, he would relinquish office.

About a hundred yards in the distance Philip spotted something and nudged me. I squinted and read: THE WEST END BAR AGAINST THE WAR written in psychedelic letters on a long narrow sign moving toward us high above the crowd. Andy, who is 6'7", was carrying the sign. Behind him moved about fifteen seedy-looking patrons of the Columbia-area bar.

Philip and I fell in behind Andy and walked along next to Sophie, who was smoking a joint and passing it down the line. I took a drag and offered it to Philip. He refused and passed it on. The West End party was dressed in their usual costumes, old Army jackets, striped railroad pants or denims, work shirts, old clothes picked up at thrift shops. Sophie looked a mess. So did Andy.

"We spent the night painting the sign," she said proudly, gazing up at the sign bobbing above the crowd, "beautiful, isn't it? An authentic work of art. It's enough to send the fascist pigs tripping their fascist pig minds."

"Some sign," I said, thinking it *really* wasn't all that good. Sophie looked cheated, so I added, "I mean I think it's the best goddamn sign here . . . or *anywhere* for that matter."

"Tell Andy then," she ordered, interrupting me, "he did most of the work, *as usual*, the real hard stuff, the *detail* work, flowers, curlicues, that kind of shit, stuff that takes *craftsmanship*. Tell Andy."

"Great sign, Andy!" I yelled. He was walking several paces ahead manfully bearing his cross.

"A heavy fucker, man," he shouted back, "don't know where the hell Rafael dug up these two-by-fours but, *Jesus*, they must weigh thirty pounds."

"Where *is* Rafael?" I asked, moving up beside Andy. He was wearing an LBJ EATS button and a bunch of wilted daisies pinned to his coat.

"Up at 113 [an SRO apartment house across from Columbia]. Got some chick there. You know that asshole, if there's no money to be made the Spic don't show. We don't need the bum anyhow."

I had expected Rafael to be at the demonstration because, while he was not a student nor a member of SDS, he was part of my group of friends at the West End.

"Got a sign?" Sophie asked, coming alongside me.

"Didn't have time to make one."

"Liar," she said, and nodded to one of the fellows in the back to bring a placard forward. The one she handed me said, "ARE YOU BOMBING WITH ME, JESUS?" It was a good sign.

"You're sticking with us, aren't you? You aren't going to join any of the pro groups?" she asked. And Andy added: "Sophie's right, man, you got to stay with us. Since you ain't an SDS creep or a veteran or mother you got no group *to* join. We have our own, man. A gas!"

"No one else *wanted* us," Sophie said sourly. "We aren't *pure* enough for SDS . . . those jokers, ha! And you *know* how the straights are," she attempted a piercing look in Philip's direction. "*That* with *you?*"

Philip was walking to my right. "Yes," I said, introducing him.

"You know how these straights are," Sophie continued bitterly, ignoring Philip except to pass him theatrical glances of contempt; she, as everyone else at the West End Bar, distrusted anything that appeared straight and they did not grow them any straighter than Philip. "God, I'd rather be marching with those prissy Communists than be part of the straights. Women Strike for Peace, blah, blah, blah." Sophie was the dark lady of the West End. Black, fuzzy hair which

24

she tried to straighten unsuccessfully with Vitalis, a tiny body, elegant, graceful little hands which seemed incongruous with her tough manner; a Jew renegade, almost anti-Semitic in her inability to admit to the existence of her Orthodox parents, in her angry condemnations of the refusal of Jewish inmates to resist their Nazi executioners, in her impassioned verbal attacks upon the Jewish shop owners in the non-white ghettos who bled the poor. Sophie was a true believer denied faith who covered her loss with a highly developed cynicism about life, making a patchwork of relationships to fill a need to belong, always getting shafted in the end. Sometimes Sophie made me believe in tribal guilt, sometimes she seemed compulsive in her need to give way to vulnerability, to place herself in the role of victim. Part of this was her intense sentimentality about her friends. That was her faith, that clean and irrevocable loyalty to her friends. And it was not the highest compliment to be loved by her, for her standards were embarrassingly low. She loved losers. Broke, busted, wiped out, piss-cleaned, horny, *weak*, against the wall, you could go to her and she gave you what she had and told you to forget the shit, fuck the System, the rest of it, each man and his bag. Beautiful, she called you, regardless.

"Baby," she said, offering me another drag, "this whole play in the park doesn't amount to a pile of shit. Doesn't mean a goddamn thing. You know what I think," she asked, looping her hand through my belt, walking close to me, her hand leashed to me, tugging at my pants for emphasis, "I think [tug] this *shitty* war [hard tug] is going to go on and I think we are schmucks [tug] to parade around the city. So the war we should *stop* [tug, tug] so we ought to start throwing bombs and killing some of the bastards who run this country. *This* [tug] is a *country?* More like a *prison* this is. Violent resistance, that's the answer. Otherwise you should shut up and play the game like this *futzface* [tug] over there." She pointed at Philip, releasing my pants.

"It doesn't do any good to kill people," Philip interjected. "That's a moral contradiction, to kill people to stop killing people." I was surprised to see Philip at the protest, now I was surprised that he would open his mouth on the side of the angels.

"So sometimes," Sophie said, "sometimes maybe you kill a few to stop the killing of the many? You must kill sometimes the killers. It *certainly* doesn't make any sense to parade around on a Saturday and listen to speeches by Uncle Tom King. That doesn't impress nobody."

There was a pause while Sophie took a deep drag on her grass, then she put her hand on my shoulder, pulling me toward her, dropping her smoke high in my face as she spoke. "We really should pull to ourselves, baby, to ourselves... move out of this crazy scene and if we fight it's hit and run, and let the whole fucking country go to hell. If you don't care, Futzface," she said, raising her voice in Philip's direction, "and you watch for your friends, then nothing can touch you."

Futzface shook his head and looked at me, smiling.

Another hour. By passing on the outside we inched our way up the line of march, moving behind a contingent of solemn mothers pushing solemn babies in baby carriages decorated with balloons and red crepe paper. We were now on the north side of Central Park South, walking toward Madison Avenue. There was a disturbance ahead at the corner of the park and Sixth Avenue so Andy put down the West End sign and I handed mine to Sophie to hold while Philip and I lit cigarettes. As we stood there waiting to go on, we heard great shouts up ahead and then thousands of people broke out of the park and rushed in mass on to Sixth Avenue, following huge red and NLF flags carried by young Trotskyite partisans. The parade was specifically prohibited from marching down any avenue but Madison, yet there before us seemingly tens of thousands of yelling, sign-bearing people were taking over Sixth, forcing startled drivers off the avenue, completely catching the cops by surprise, stopping traffic. It was an impressive sight suddenly to stop and hear shouting and to see several score flags being swung into the traffic, the traffic halting and then splitting out of the way making a path for a crowd of Leftists pouring out of the park. Philip and I looked at each other. "Come on, Dotson, let's see what it's about. Come on." And off he went.

"Where the hell are you going?" Sophie shouted, as Philip and I ran to join the Trotskyite contingent flooding down Sixth Avenue. "You're going to get your heads busted!" I looked back to see Andy replace the sign on his shoulder, Sophie standing beside him holding my "ARE YOU BOMBING WITH ME, JESUS?" sign aloft in her hands, he towering over her, the West End sign towering over them both, the West End patrons straggling beat out behind them, following the carriage-pushing mothers along the park. I waved and yelled, "Peace, Sophie!" and Sophie dropped the sign and lifted both arms in an Eisenhower-type salute. I turned and ran to catch up with Philip.

About twenty thousand people poured out of Central Park behind those beautiful flags, spontaneously seizing the avenue, shouting and singing as they marched illegally on to Times Square. Philip and I trotted about a hundred yards behind the first line of march—the flags fluttering, the staffs tilted forward slightly against the wind, carried by long-haired youths, some in motorcycle helmets, some in boots and thick denim trousers, surrounded by a squad of tough-looking girls screaming peace slogans hoarsely at their side—Philip's coat open and flapping in the wind, his face flushed with tension, appearing happy, shouting with the marchers, "Hey, hey, LBJ, how many kids did you kill today?" this All-American Episcopalian Republican Ivy League Fraternity Man, his pre-law schedule set, his future to be weighted with the profit of easing corporations around the law, shouted PEACE NOW at the office workers leaning out of Saturday windows over the street, the shoppers standing hesitant and confused on the sidewalks, caught by surprise, the drivers sitting trapped on side streets, fuming at the delay, cursing the cops and the Communists and the dirty faggot hippie punks, pressing on their horns. "Philip," I yelled, "you're aiding and abetting the Communist Conspiracy!" He threw his hands in the air. "Shit!" he answered. "What?" He grinned, and then cupped his hands over his mouth, shouting a few feet from my ear, "I said I don't give a shit!" I laughed. We marched on, the crowd swelling behind us, Times Square drawing near. At 52nd Street a cab driver jumped from his taxi and attacked one of the marchers. We went on. A woman screamed at us from a crowd of spectators under a theatre marquee: "Why don't you get a bath, you filthy beatniks!" I glanced over at Philip. We laughed.

It was exciting running down Sixth Avenue. It was exciting shouting, "Hell!No!We! Won't! Go!" at the tourists and astonished straights who stood wide-eyed watching the Leftists take to the streets, raising our fingers in a victory salute at the cops who had given in to our act and were reduced to doing their best to help clear the traffic from our path, obviously made nervous by the sudden appearance of the radical crowd, the motherfuckers outnumbered at last, stranded for a moment with the traffic, unable to get at our heads; and I could not help feeling theatrically revolutionary, thinking of Paris street-fighting and of the incidents which give rise to revolt in the cities; I could not help feeling good because we were strong, in greater mass than anyone else, solid, momentarily triumphant, making the goddamn cops smooth the way for us. It was good for a time to think we were winning.

When the march reached Times Square there was a great cheer as the revolutionary flags swung east on to 42nd Street, whipping under the Allied Chemical Tower, the electric sign rolling the news across the face of the building, LIFE blinking on and off, the traffic snarled, the hustlers and derelicts standing stupefied by our appearance. Romantic. Dangerously so, the flags and chanting and raised fists drawing the adrenalin, creating the feeling of omnipotence that comes when your side invades the center of the city and holds captive the physical symbols of power. I looked over at Philip, captive of our enthusiasm. He also was blowing high, tripping out, giving way.

At 42nd Street a few fist fights broke out near Bryant Park. Near Stern's department store a group of Cuban exiles broke into the march, tearing up signs, riot making. Philip yelled, "Let's stay close!" At the Public Library several kids broke ranks and climbed upon the 42nd Street door fixing a red flag to the building, announcing, "The Public Library is ours!" We cheered and surged on. Beautiful. It was our day. The red and NLF banners flying far in front, the crowd pushing on to the United Nations. At that moment, watching Philip run beside me, possessed by the excitement of the march, shouting with us, "End the War! End the War!" driven by the emotion of owning the New York streets for once in our lives, hurling out our anger—new to Philip—at our reactionary country, with its fearful indifference to the desperation of its native poor, its callous, wicked disregard of the victims of and in our America. God Bless America. Anger discovered at the institutions which strip our lives of power and purpose, delimiting our future, defining, deadening, absorbing our freedom distantly. At that moment I was filled with a curiously ambivalent love for the country, for the woman standing on the trunk of her car screaming, "Bomb Hanoi!" for the shoppers who returned our victory salute, raising their hands above their heads, waving at us, for the people stranded on buses locked in place by our action, who sat confused and appalled as we raced by; and love, too, for Philip's enthusiasm, and for the red flags moving ahead of us and for the country which reluctantly allowed them to fly. God Bless America.

I do not know why Philip shouted then as he did, but I think there is something regressive and childish about public demonstrations, about the chanting and the posturing strength. It is a kind of theatre, with banners and songs and ritualistic language, a moment unto itself creating the illusion of power, absolutist, making the unreal, the wished-for, seem within reach. It is a place where one can say things and mean them which one could never speak anywhere else. It is mime where one, protected by the anonymity of great numbers, takes up the poses of his neighbors and adopts the attitude and speech of the mass. It is theatre creating an implacable need for command.

At Third Avenue and 42nd Street I swung around and looked at the crowd following us. The street was packed as far west as I could see. "Look, Philip," I yelled, "look at that beautiful crowd!" He glanced over his shoulder. "God! What a *mob!*"

As we passed the *Daily News* building we shouted, "Fascist press!" and we laughed. Ahead of us the flags were nearing First Avenue, the East River just beyond, the United Nations to the north hidden behind the apartment houses of Tudor City. And then the noise of the first line, lowering the flags as they crossed under the pedestrian bridge on to First, their shouts of "Peace" echoing to us.

Suddenly behind us there was a great deal of screaming. Philip grabbed my arm, "Jesus! Look!" and pointed back to Second Avenue. A block west, at the intersection of Second and 42nd, fifty mounted police had ridden into the intersection and were driving into the marchers, scattering them north, splitting the parade into two sections, isolating us from the majority behind. The first section, oblivious to the police action, continued to follow the flags toward First Avenue. They numbered about a thousand. Philip and I, fearing the horsemen might turn and ride into our ranks, ran east, working our way into the front contingent. And then before us, perhaps fifty yards in front, we saw the flags topple forward. Screaming was heard. Philip stared at me. "Now what?"

"Come on," I said to him, and we hurried toward the flags, making it under the pedestrian bridge. There we stopped. Before us hundreds of police were beating peace demonstrators who were trying to escape. Rightists had moved in on the assault and were busily ripping apart the revolutionary flags, tearing up our signs and clubbing an occasional demonstrator in the process. We were trapped. I was piss-scared. Philip looked horrified, his face blanched, rigid, looking like some terrified prep school kid who had stumbled unwittingly into a drunken street brawl. The access route down First Avenue was blocked by police vans, the uptown exit was sealed with manned barricades (behind which the Peter Fechter Brigade and other Rightists yelled encouragement at the cops); and bringing up the rear, riding fast down 42nd Street, galloping like out-of-shape Lone Rangers, twirling their riot sticks in the air, came New York's very own leather-armored Texas Rangers.

Philip and I crowded together, pressing as closely as possible to the wall of the bridge, and watched the police swing into the demonstrators methodically. When the mounted police reached the scene Philip and I made a dash toward the uptown barricades. Too late. A couple of the cops grabbed Philip, one clubbing him. He fell to the pavement, tearing the sleeve of his suit jacket. Hundreds of people were scattering aimlessly in panic in the sealed area, trying to escape, looking like cattle in a pen, while the cops picked them off one by one.

When I saw Philip fall I swung around and went to him, bending low, my hands over my head, bobbing toward him. "Are you hurt?" I said, asking the obvious. "The stinking bastards," he said, "the fascist bastards." I helped him to his feet and we started walking toward the northeast barricades. We were out from under the bridge now, the United Nations

31

stood directly north, *our* brothers and sisters filling the streets before it petitioning for a redress of grievances and listening to speeches while that appropriate standard of corporate liberalism—the Con Ed smoke stacks—pumped tons of pollution into the air. Distantly we could faintly hear Martin King preach: "Let us save our national honor—stop the bombing ... the American people are not vainglorious conquerors—stop the bombing!" At that point I was knocked to the ground by a nicely aimed police club to my neck. *Whack!* The comic strip stars ... pretty lights ... Philip's face ... a trickle of blood below his earlobe ... Philip helped me up ... to the barricades ... painted gray ... arguing with the cops to pass through ... moving clumsily through a crowd of Rightists holding (wouldn't you know it?) a rosary service in the small park beyond the barricades ... hundred of fascists ... "coexistence is permanent war!" ... the Battle Hymn of the Republic coming over the loudspeaker ... my head throbbing ... da dum da dum da dum ... Philip and I making our way through the crowd, followed by a dozen other peace marchers ... I noticed drops of blood had fallen on Philip's shirt collar ... "we got to sit down," I said, worried for him ... an Oriental priest said the rosary wearing an American Legion hat praying for the Captive Nations beyond the borders of God's Country ... Cubans with INVADE CUBA signs kneeling on the steps before Isaiah prophecy engraved in the stone ... "They shall beat their swords into plowshares ... Nation shall not lift up sword against Nation, neither shall they learn war anymore" ... the cops would not let us go on to the U.N. rally ... we climbed the stairs to Tudor City ... a Cuban spit at Philip ... "Fascist pig," Philip said ... down below in the tiny park the priest droned on, the crowd began to attack the peace people behind us in the park, the priest droned on. ...

We walked through Tudor City and after about three blocks we stopped and sat down on a bench and lit cigarettes and Philip took out his handkerchief and held it to the side of his head, over the wound drying, his hair appearing blonder over the white cloth. My head felt as if it were splitting. We sat there hating the cops and the war people and the Cuban exiles, and Philip muttering, "those fucking bastards," at no one in particular. We stood up and walked over to 42nd Street and Second Avenue. A boy, about twelve years old, strutted by with a hand-painted sign: WAR IS A BAD TRIP.

We stood at the intersection of 42nd Street and Second Avenue. I was tired. Philip seemed about worn through. The sky was clouding over heavily. Soon it would rain. There were many police standing around, cocky, flipping their penis clubs up and down, kings of the fucking hill.

A young man in his late teens walked into the intersection against the light. He cried, "Peace Now!" Philip and I waved at him. I thought, he must have just arrived, he must not have seen the bust or he would not shout like that. He must not know what the police have done. He was wearing a light blue shirt and blue pants. His hair was sandy colored. He was about 5'10". As he entered the street he shouted the slogan. That was all he did. Then four pro-war men jumped him. One kicked him in the groin. The young man slumped down as he was kicked. I thought, you poor bastard, you better just lie there, you better not move. There were many police in the area. The pro-war men ran away. The young man got up and tried to chase after them. You dumb kid, I thought, they'll get you now. We did nothing. As he started up, four policemen suddenly attacked him. They beat him. The young man fell to the street. Philip said, "Good Christ, they're animals." The young man got up. They hit him again. He broke free of the police and ran uptown along Second Avenue toward 43rd Street, weaving dazed to the right and left. We followed him as he ran. About a third of the way to 43rd the police caught him. We saw the police beat him senseless, using their fists, not their clubs, feeling the thud of the knuckle against the stomach. Nice. Finally they knocked him unconscious, dropping him bloody against the curb. They looked about, daring any of the spectators to intervene. We were within ten feet of the young man. We jeered at the police, my head throbbing as I yelled, saying, "Shame!" and "Bullies!" We wanted them to leave the young man alone. And then, unable ever to release a victim, they lifted the unconscious boy. Two officers dragged him to a mounted policeman nearby. They lifted the limp body nearly as high as the saddle of the horse. The young man's bleeding head was slumped forward, his chin resting on his chest. I could see the blood slipping out under his shirt sleeve and running down his hand and dripping on to the pavement. While the two patrolmen held him the mounted trooper raised his nightstick above his head and brought it down on the boy's skull swiftly. He hit him very hard. We heard the crack of the wooden club against his skull. A woman screamed. Philip said, "My God, it's incredible!" My stomach began to hurt. We were frightened. They dropped the body to the pavement. He was bleeding heavily. The police pushed us away. For the first time in his life Philip was terrified of the cops. Their violence unprovoked. Obscene. Cheap.

We went north and then over to the United Nations. We worked our way through the crowd. We sat on the curb. Stokeley said, "There is a higher law than the law of the racist McNamara; there is a higher law than the law of the fool Dean Rusk; there is a higher law than the law of the buffoon Lyndon Baines Johnson." And in Atlanta Hubert Humphrey was saying, "America needs to tell the world of the lives it is saving. We need to be known as a nation of peacemakers, not peace marchers!" Hurrah!

It began to rain. Philip and I took a bus up to Columbia and we went to his room and we took a shower and we lay down. His head hurt. So did mine.

chapter three

LATER THAT EVENING I WALKED OVER TO THE WEST
End Bar, leaving Philip curled up on the floor, his head on a
pillow, the handkerchief bandage hanging loosely over his ear,
seeming very young lying naked on the rug, his arms tucked
between his thighs, his feet curled under his bottom. Very
young and blond and WASP and utterly clean and removed
from street brawls and loudmouthed pigskin cops and other
darkly fierce tokens of repression which the poor and black
and homosexual and angered and Leftist and nonconformist
young know everyday. American all his life—his forebears
probably squatted on tribal lands here on this shore four
centuries before—and only today he woke to America. I stood
and looked at him a moment and then reluctantly covered
him with a blanket from the bed.

I left him a note telling him I had gone to the bar and
suggested that he stop in at the Health Service at Saint Luke's
Hospital to have his injury examined when he got up. I had
slept about four hours, my head felt better, but now I was
horny as hell (one of the curious side effects of the experience
of violence, at least for me, is that its creates sexual hunger.
Michel, traveling the road from Ravello to Sorrento in Gide's
The Immoralist, beats up the coachman and that act permits
him, for the first time, to possess his wife. The violence was

35

liberating. I do not know what the coachman did after the battering but I suppose, like me, he went to a saloon to hustle up some action).

The West End Bar was jammed with Columbia students, weary professors from the School of General Studies (which is perhaps the most radical faculty of the University's divisions), plus the usual contingent of heads and lonely old people who drift in nightly from their tiny soiled rooms in Columbia-owned SRO buildings. It was that period in the semester between the end of midterm exams and the beginning of finals when students go lazy for awhile and rebellious and doubt the value of structured education and drink more and smoke more and grow conscious of the waning of the school year and the opportunities lost and the quota of flesh never reached. The jocks express the discontent with sex and beer and frat parties and tacky Barnard College mixers and new clothes and a willingness to fight. The rest of us do it with an increasingly morbid sensitivity to political cynicism, public complaints about meaninglessness and frustration, sex and the fielding of wilder, higher trips toward a final, treacherously blown mind. Our sole commonality is in the area of sexual taste. There it ends.

On the make that night, thinking that finals aren't for five weeks yet and papers aren't due and anyway it's spring and we all get less than we deserve. God *knows* after a winter of playing with our dongs—kids again, behind the bathroom door pulling off into toilet paper, sheets, towels, old *Playboys*, Dixie cups, underwear, zipping it on the goddamn floor— hell, after *that* we deserve a little piece, we deserve some human *consideration*. On the make, thinking I could use the whack on the head as a sympathy ploy, doing the tour, a kind of voyeuristic round-the-world, circling the goddamn bar, watching the people slide their trays on the runner before the steam table ordering corn beef or lox or stew or Special Cut 100% U. S. Inspected Beef ¼ pound hamburgers, walking past the junior critics brooding prophets in the Kierkegaard Corner by the men's room, their predictions and bias as dim as the lighting, cruising the washouts from Barnard, the ugliest, hairiest, most desexed, over-intellectualized sluts on God's green earth, our *sister* school, for Christ's sake, thinking what have we done, Sweet Lord, to get stuck with *Barnard* . . . and my mother wonders why Columbia has the only homophile club in existence and why the dormitories swarm with faggots and psyched-out onanists and the library bathrooms give the boys combat training for Fire Island. She wonders. Has she *never* seen Barnard? Is there no pity?

I checked the booths, took a look in the back room, even— yes, I had fallen *that* low—studied the graffiti on the men's room wall, taking my time about it, reading carefully, hoping for a new name and address (how little we ask of life), perhaps a phone number uncalled scrawled somewhere unappreciated. Nothing but the usual phallic dimensions, the forlorn gay pleas, the walls owned as everywhere by nelliesize queens and pushy numbers begging for trade (why isn't the heterosexual as generous with public information?). Defeated I went to the bar and sat on a stool near the entrance, as far as possible from Bob Dylan schlumping *Rainy Day Woman* through the juke box across the room. Sidney, who owned the joint, liked the music loud because he believed it made the place *seem* fuller. *Fuller!* As if it were not enough to have us pounded tightly together in his little bar, laid like cord wood one on top the other. Big Spenders! Stuffing dollar bills in Sid's itchy hands. He loved the feel of paper money.

I ordered a scotch and water, asking specifically for J & B, since I never trusted bar scotch. I lit a cigarette, the first I had smoked since I awoke at Philip's, and the fumes sent my head spinning and I remembered the *feel* of the nightstick on my neck, the confusion of that moment, the terror. And strangely I thought of a pornographic peek-freak book I had seen in one of the dorms a week before with drawings of im-

37

possibly hung, grandbagged Green Berets slouching manfully before Vietcong prisoners who moved in adoration before their government-inspected baskets feeling the family jewels. The homosexual vision, startlingly honest, seeing the war alone as one gang-banging pricknic, a leathering S & M orgy. Rough trade in boots. And I wondered if at that moment the fruit stand had reassembled on Central Park West and if the plainclothesmen, dressed like college boys or prick peddlers (laundry in place), loving it (authority and violence condoned and sex guiltless and self-righteousness combined with the badge) were working the belles and broncos toward detention and blackmail. The cops. In the life unadmitted.

And the Mamas and Papas came through melting in with "Monday, Monday" and I felt tired and vulnerable to sentiment, missing Philip oddly and missing the cops' clopping, distant violence; and I thought of sitting in the West End six months before with lovely Rachel and listening to the Mamas and Papas and Rachel telling me of her last depression and the six weeks in the mental ward of Saint Luke's and how she was dropping out, unable to face the shit anymore, the smile not working, the stiff upper lip gone, the future blighted and corrupt, love unseized; and her going to Berkeley soon after and one month later driving to the middle of the bridge and stopping her car and jumping into the Bay. And to this day I do not know why she did it. But there was something similar in her desperation and discomfort to that of the nighttime homosexuals fanning along the park and to the kids who in need of revolt face the cops. There was no relief in this country for any of them.

No relief. I thought about the afternoon's march and the clubbing and Philip's remarkable anger and his ability in the shortest time to become other than he was. He converted. What was improbable for him before the flags broke down Sixth Avenue, before the whip on the head, became actual.

Of the many moderate students who chose against their

past to side with us, Philip's conversion (for that is what it was) was the first I witnessed. It was public and quick, completed in an afternoon. In the process of growing up in our country—in the simple fact that he matured when he did—he confronted the essential indecency of industrial capitalism and facing it *consciously* for the first time he either had to deny its existence and accommodate himself to the pattern of the System, reducing his life to corporate forms, destroying his manhood, or he had to choose to act in rebellion, placing himself consciously in opposition to the dominant values of American society.

For Philip, as for many other moderate, quietly alienated young men, manhood would be acquired in resistance on the Left. In denial. Carrying four centuries of white guilt, reminded continually of his implication in present injustice, he would tempt expiation through violence. For the problem of the young white is to create personhood while at the same time finding relief from tribal guilt, guilt whose victims clutter the ghettos of urban America. For them redemption is in rebellion. There alone. The tragedy of the United States may be that it has come to face its own iniquity only to discover that its institutions allow no reprieve.

At the West End I thought about Philip and his choice and the awful difficulty of keeping integrity, refusing to sell out in a nation of shopkeepers and corporate pimps copping out. And I wondered, Jesus, if it was worth the price to be lamb's pure on these shores.

I ordered another drink and looked around the bar. Sid was having the place redecorated and while the décor was not much improved (unless you consider Authentic Ye Olde English Pub an improvement) the prices were worse. When you complained to Sid about the prices he charged in his joint, this he said: "I gotta live. I should worry about losing the business of a few schmucky kids . . . you know what this lease is worth, this location? A little increase in prices don't hurt nobody, not with my overhead, color television, loans to deadbeat Mr. Smarty students. A success it is when tourist buses line up outside. Gray Line buses with *wheel*thy goyim. . . ." Sid came up as I was sitting over the bar, my elbows on the counter, and inquired about the parade.

"So how did it go, Dotson?" he asked, absentmindedly rearranging the glasses on the bar as he spoke, his round, bald head sparkling with sweat under the new, imported lighting ("The real thing, pal, very expen*sive*. . . . I ain't joking. You laugh, I should waste money on beatniks with *my* family and bills? *Expensive*, like at the Concord").

"It went fine, Sid. The usual. Couple kids got beat up." I liked Sid. For all his complaining about how we abused him and took advantage of his hopeless generosity, he was a good man. You could always bum a meal off him if the need were there. "You're a nice guy, Sid," I said, remembering my appreciation of him.

"Nice, schmice! A rich man, better rich than nice." And he dismissed my compliment with a languid, long swish of the hand downward. A hand shrug. "I bet those *coppers* wasn't so nice."

"No, Sid, not so nice."

"The coppers!" he said angrily, and then, dismissing them with a shrug of helplessness, asked me, "I hear that Mr. Preacher Billy Graham will come to the University next week. You bring him?"

I nodded. I was chairman of a speakers bureau at Columbia, *Humanitas*, and Billy Graham was one of the speakers we had scheduled.

"Maybe you bring him in the West End after for drinks and a little food?" I could see Sid adding up the profit and publicity in his head.

"He doesn't drink, Sid." Disappointment. Only a Christian would not drink.

"He don't drink?" his arms spread wide, eyebrows raised in

astonishment. "Oy gut, the man's crazy he don't drink." With that Sid left me to my drink.

Sophie came up and put her arms around my neck, leaning heavily, inadvertently pressuring the place where I had been clubbed.

"Getting drunk again? A regular rummy?" she giggled in my ear. I shook my head No. "Where's the blond *ass*ristocrat?" she asked, sounding more than a trifle blurred and gone as if she had been smoking mary jane heavily, which was probably what she had been doing.

"He's in his room. I just left him there asleep. Received a bad clubbing at the march."

"Where, man?" Andy asked, towering to her right. I had not noticed him. "We didn't see nobody club nobody."

"By the U.N." I explained, turning toward him and easing Sophie off my neck. "Remember the group that broke down Sixth Avenue . . . remember? The red flags?" Andy also was high.

"The Trotskyists?" Sophie asked, clearing her mind.

"Yeah. Well, at 42nd Street the police attacked and Philip got caught in it. God, he's mad as hell."

"Serves him right, the straight. Maybe he'll learn something about this fucking country," Sophie let it fly, "this goddamn putzsucking stupid country, fascist. . . ."

"Come on, baby," I said, putting my arm around her, "let's get ourselves into a booth, then you can bitch to your heart's content."

"I'm not *bitching*. I'm making a patriotic observation." She and Andy and I went to the back of the bar and took a booth. I carried my drink over and Andy went to the bar to get himself a glass of milk and Sophie a Coke. While he was gone I asked Sophie if he were staying with her tonight. Bad news as she was, I needed badly to be held that night.

"Why not? What's wrong with little Andy?" She was

offended, I think in part because I had never asked her before, never like that implying I wanted her free for me.

"Nothing's wrong with him. I just wondered."

"*Now* you wonder! I've known you three years and a lot of hell, Sweetheart, and now tonight when I got Andy, you pick tonight to wonder." She spoke harshly.

"Baby," I said softly, angling too obviously for sympathy, "I was hit this afternoon by the fucking cops. See." I turned around to expose the damage. She appeared *very* unimpressed.

"You maybe learn to stay away from amateur straights ... bourgeois bastards with their schmaltzy manners and view of the world. You ought to know America's no big rock candy mountain." I did not respond. I was tired of politics and of venting hatred against the corruption of our country's masters. I wanted to make love. Period. Sophie sensed my quiet and stopped talking and let her eyes appraise me kindly. "What *is* wrong, Sweetheart, did it hurt that much?"

"No, Sophie, it wasn't the cops. Not that...." And then Andy interrupted, returning with the milk and Coke and bringing in tow his friend, Roger. Andy sat next to me. Roger slid in beside Sophie.

"Dotson got banged on the head by the cops this afternoon. I think his feelings are hurt," she informed Roger.

"How did it happen?" he asked, the tone of his voice monotonous, level, direct, causing one to wonder if he would pull out a newsman's pad and pencil and take an interview. Roger never sounded involved. But then, being a Dialectical Materialist (in the same way priests are Thomist), with not a little Stalinism in his veins, he considered involvement in personal problems threatening. Without the guts to join the Party, or perhaps with too much integrity, he acted *as if* he were a member on a kind of sabbatical functioning as commissar keeping us leftwing humanists in line. In short he was, as were many of his peers in SDS, a purist. And that, friends, was a real pain in the ass.

42

"Well, Roger, about twenty thousand Trotskyites, see, and other assorted bogeymen broke ranks and went shooting down Sixth Avenue and the pigs cut them up. Philip and I getting cut along with the rest of the sheep."

"You're all nuts," Roger commented, after a suitably professorial pause. "Down Sixth Avenue like that bourgeoise Sunday School parade was a *serious* event, an authentic revolutionary situation."

"Sorry, Roger."

"Fools," he snorted in his best Grand Inquisitor manner, humorless as always. "Utterly lacking in discipline."

"We wanted to stop the goddamn war, Roger. That's all." It sounded absurd outloud.

"Yeah, Rog," Andy interjected, "how the hell was they to know the motherfuckers was going to bust 'em? Huh?"

"Trotskyites! Leftwing adventurists!" Roger continued, ignoring his question. "And then you wonder why the proletarian Left loses."

"Baby," Sophie said, touching Roger's hand, "it was your proletarian Left that was dropping cement on us. It was the holy workers who shouted about bombing Hanoi."

"They're misguided. Duped. Bribed by the capitalist ruling circles. It wasn't a revolutionary situation and, if you value the war against imperialism, you wouldn't have messed with that thoroughly disgusting middle-class picnic." That a boy, Roger. The loyal party functionary to the bitter end. Doctrinaire. A born bureaucrat. He was a combination of the early Leon Trotsky, without the passion, and a branch librarian. He incessantly held up to us a Higher Marxist Vision, a revolutionary ethic and system only *he* really understood. I sometimes thought he rather saw himself as a prophet without honor in his own country with Columbia being his Swiss exile on the way to some future Finland Station. Sadly, Roger's trouble was the trouble of the age. There was no party of the young and therefore no snug bureaucracy to advance in.

What organization there was—for example, SDS—was an impossible situation for a man who demanded theoretical and organizational neatness. SDS was hopelessly unsystematic in doctrine, its ideology (if one could call it that) being a confusion of anarchistic, Marxist, Populist, syndicalist, utopian wishes for a future America. Its unity lay not in a concrete vision of a future society (although there was broad agreement on the outlines of such a newer world: participatory democracy, freedom from hunger and ignorance, wide liberties, the destruction of the concentrations of wealth) but in contingent, situationalist solidarity. Its members came together to fight this particular war or oppose that specific injustice leaving the future in question. What they alone had in common was an implacable demand for accountability on the part of the masters of the earth. The rich, the executioners, the makers of imperialist policy, the enforcers of racism were to be made answerable for their acts. That included the Soviet totalitarian imperialists and the fascists and the corporate liberals and the other statists who act against man. To this end they worked to dislocate the functioning of American institutions in order that in the chaos true freedom would appear. While Roger half agreed theoretically, his heart was unconvinced. It was too Romantic. Too emotional. Poor Roger, he applied himself to the task of ordering the radical cause only to discover daily that a bureaucratic, Stalinist mind did not function efficiently in a movement as fundamentally nihilist in tendency as SDS. But Roger, bless his heart, kept giving it the old college try.

"Shut up, stupid," Andy said to Roger, "we ain't interested and we ain't in the mood for one of your shitty lectures."

Roger looked in bewilderment at Andy and sighed, shaking his head. "I wasn't *lecturing*, Andy, I was attempting to place the Mobilization parade in perspective, to explain what it actually was. What it was was a congregation of liberals and leftwing adventurists playing revolutionary in the park. That

44

is all. An ego exercise. It was most *un*political." His voice shuddering with disdain. With that Roger stood up and left without so much as a good-bye. I watched to see if he would shake the dust off his shoes as he went out. He didn't.

"That one's a spook," Sophie said, "and I don't mind saying that he gives me the shitass creeps. He's the kind of nutzy that runs camps making people into bars of soap and doesn't think it's wrong because it fits some crazy plan."

I finished my drink. I told Sophie I was deadtired and wanted to go home. I kissed her good night and play-punched Andy on the arm as I left.

It was cool outside. No traffic. Clumps of students wandered between the cafés on Broadway. Drunks and homeless old men slept off the night on the benches by the stunted trees on the traffic islands. I was lonely. I wanted to bed someone very badly. I thought Philip might know of something floating free tonight so I walked down to his place. He was not at home. I missed him.

I walked back to Broadway and then cut over and went on to campus and walked along College Walk under the trees. I sat for a while on the sundial feeling very abandoned and self-pitying. The lawns of Columbia are very wide and long and at night the lights filter against the pollution in the air and spread a soft white haze over the grass. And you sit on the sundial in the center of campus and behind you, misted, is Butler Library, massive, square, unoriginal in design, a fortress, and the dormitories flickering beside it in the distance behind the trees, letting out tiny noises of phonograph records and argument and laughter from the rooms. Ahead on the knoll looms the columned Low Library, the administration building, where power sits indifferent to our pursuits, detached, coded, ancient, aloof. I loved Columbia, its walks at night, its sounds, the chapel and the Van Am and Lewisohn quads, the spaciousness of its South Lawn. As I sat there forgetting

45

the march in the afternoon and the charge of the police against my friends and forgetting the arrogance and venality of the Trustees and the University's racist policies toward Harlem, its complicity, by its participation in the Pentagon's Institute for Defense Analysis and the CIA fundings, in the very war we marched against hours before, sitting there, Christ, I loved the goddamn place.

I had been at Columbia four years. A transfer student. Like everybody else I hated the bureaucracy of the institution, its capriciousness, the sense of being unnamed, disregarded, unable ever to enter into the policy process that established the borders of my life. Each time I registered, filling out the goddamn forms, giving the University mounting nuisance information about my personal life and beliefs, signing the government's draft deferment cards—class ranking—the medical service forms, the rest of it, being sent from place to place for hours, for hours waiting in lines going by number, being victim of the bitchery and stupidity of the Bursar's Office and Financial Aid Office and the Dean's Office. Each time, before being processed through like a commodity, never knowing for sure whether the Powers That Be would allow me back (then it was financial, academic and legal determinants. A year later political considerations entered in); each semester my disgust with the System grew. In addition, as I became active in Leftist student organizations, I was made aware of the grievances of the lowest employees of the University, denied bargaining rights, denied a union, working for the worst wages, and the grievances of students hurt by administrative whim, denied due process, without adequate appeal.

My first year at Columbia I fell under the influence of Daniel Dodson, a Comparative Literature professor. He was, in terms of what I now believe to be truth, the seminal influence on my life. Daniel Dodson. Black-gray curly hair. His face fatigued and handsome. Outrageous in the gentlest way. Shy. Fated. Filled. Burma. India. Dropping munitions. Hating

46

war. Acting irrevocably beyond reprieve, of loss, of unaccountable remorse. Like every other student who came into contact with him I was taken by his compassion and his certitude and honesty and the charming modesty of his truth. He paid for what he knew. I took every goddamn course he gave, read his books, listened to him, learned. For I needed then something to replace a faith disengaged. He was an existential humanist. I became one. He continually criticized the brutality and sickness of the American nation. I accepted what he said. He taught that we ought to stand with the victims. I tried.

I bugged him at home, followed him around, made a goddamn pest out of myself. Daniel Dodson had what I needed —a rational explanation of the human predicament and an ethic that commanded action and provided meaning. It was purpose I was after. He opposed the war in Vietnam from the beginning. He spoke against the viciousness of our society. I learned to do it. When one has been without place and truth for a long time and then one moves toward it, one becomes an evangelist for what one has embraced.

I took a taxi down to the Village and went to two bars and finally picked up a piece in the Ninth Circle and took it home. At last I got some love mileage out of the cop's knock on the head.

The next morning Philip called. He was strangely elated by the triumph of having had several stitches sewn in his scalp. He told me part of his head was shaved and he considered it his red badge of courage.

"What are you going to do now, Philip?"

"About what?"

"The war."

He laughed and paused and then went into about ten minutes of solid profanity against the System and the cops

47

and the President and the Congress and the Vice President and the University.

"I need to learn, Dotson. You see I don't know enough. This may sound funny but I hate the bastards who run this country, I hate the war. And I want to learn why I hate them."

"Don't you know why?"

"What I mean, is that I want to be able to say why. I can *feel* why but I want to be able to tell it. I want to know what to do. I want to know *why* America is this way and why it doesn't change."

I told him to call the SDS office downtown and go by and pick up some literature. I also gave him several titles to read. I said I wanted to talk with him. He agreed to meet me at the luncheon we were giving for Billy Graham. "I'll have some tough questions for that son of a bitch," he said. I knew he would.

chapter four

PHILIP WENT HOME TO SPEND THE SUMMER IN Haverford, lounging around the big house watching baseball on television, forgetting commitment . . . the others drifted away. Without bread I stayed in New York and got a part-time job I did not intend to keep, took a course in Columbia Summer Session, audited a course at the New School, cut most of the classes at both institutions, loafed, nursed over-priced drinks at Max's Kansas City, girl-watched, fell in love for three weeks with a girl from San Francisco named Michelle (my sister's name), faded on the grass. Sophie went to Mexico, taking Andy along as Male Companion and Visiting Head, and entered a colony of mary jane enthusiasts across the border in Lower California, non-revolutionary but incredibly high.

During the summer the only notable thing that happened to me was meeting Al, a member not in good standing of the Student Afro-American Society at Columbia, a blacks-only organization founded in 1964 to serve as a lobbying group for the few blacks (perhaps two hundred) in the student body of seventeen thousand. The black students were on a Black-Is-Beautiful kick, trying to shoot into each other's injured egos massive doses of forced pride to counter the feelings of inadequacy and defeatism which being a nigger in white America gives you.

Al was special for a number of reasons, besides the obvious one of being one of the few blacks in the junior class. Unlike his fellow Black-Is-Beautiful brothers, Al did not protest too much. He was not racially arrogant (maybe being endlessly told to remember your place makes you arrogant when you discover that your place is a slum ghetto and the Man giving it to you is sucking your money with inflated prices and impossible terms; maybe trying to make your place anew forces you into overcompensation and protective arrogance. But there is no getting around the fact that some black students, while it is understandable, were a pain in the ass to be around with their crapping about White Guilt and fixing the garbage and death and brokenness on you, never crediting your heart— i.e., intentions—with a damn thing, treating you like a honkey motherfucker whether you were one or not. Most whites responded to this kind of racist arrogance by prostrating their guilt and getting down on their knees and kissing black ass. But I always thought it was as bad to be a slave as a master and that we were not going to become men until we cut out this racist sin and forgiveness shit and started treating each other like men). Al never played the racial S & M game, partly because he was a homosexual, a victim twice, and thus had an extra portion of tolerance in his beautiful mind, and partly because he was so damn sure of himself. Perhaps all of the ego-deprived ought to follow him and hustle their ass down Third Avenue, because when the Man begs to pay real coin to go down on your thing, it does something to reaffirm your value, at least it did for Al.

That summer both Al and I worked in the Times Square area, I was a switchboard operator at a private club (WASP only) and he as a clerk in one of the quasi-porno bookstores that grace Midtown, giving New York much of the gaudy sex-air that voyeuristic tourists love to bend their minds inside, the color that makes Fun City such a nice place to visit. Al had the better job by far.

I met Al one night when I went peep-freaking in his shop and started talking to him and discovered he went to Columbia and knew people I knew and lived near the university. One evening he took me up to his apartment. I met his roommate, a kid about eighteen, white, blond, green-eyed, who had come to New York from Idaho a year before and had never met a Negro—reminding me of me—until he came to Sodom and saw Al far down on Greenwich Avenue late one night and while the women howled and screeched from the upper floors of the House of Detention Al and his white trick ambled into Howard Johnson's men's room and fell in love. Yes, New York Is A Summer Festival.

The roommate, Jerry, was Idaho dumb. Verbally sloppy. Forgetting that Al was black he dished things like, "Look at *that* nigger!" and "*Who* does that *dinge* queen think she *is?*" Al never appeared to mind. Tolerant. In love.

Late one night I walked Al home from the West End Bar. This was in the late summer, August, the night was warm and the tide was up and we walked down Riverside Drive, watching the lights from the hideous apartment towers in hideous New Jersey play on the water. "When I was a kid," Al said, picking up a rock and sending it spinning across the West Side Highway, not quite reaching the water, the George Washington Bridge spanning the Hudson delicately, like spider's thread, to the north, "I used to come down here from Harlem . . . take the train down and get off at the Columbia stop and come over here to the park and watch the white kids play, some even had governesses in frilly uniforms. I come and the Man made me feel like black shit, made me *know* I didn't belong on no whitey's street with *his* honkey kids. Christ, I don't know, I come down here and come down here and I wanted so goddamn bad one day to live in one of them motherfuckers' apartments . . . I never even saw a room where

51

people *lived* that had wall-to-wall rugs until I came to Columbia. Never. I wanted what he had, wanted my black kids walked in the Riverside Park by *white* governesses in frilly uniforms. So bad."

I asked him if he still wanted it.

"No more, man, no more, no more. I'm done with that scene, no soul, bloodless. I'm done swimming after the Man. Now to make the bastards pay, you know?"

"What, the whites, make the whites pay?"

"It ain't white and it ain't black. It's rich and it's poor. It's the oppressed and the oppressors. That's all! And, baby, if you start believing," Al said, tight, the anger close, constant, closer and more intimate than it ever was for me, "really *believing* that it is because the Man's *white* that he's the Man, shit, then you start thinking it's because you're *black* you're a nigger. I tell you, being a *nigger* has nothing to do with color, it has to do with being *kept* dumb and made different... if there weren't blacks around in their America they'd find someone else to play nigger. Not blacks in the Midwest so the fuckers choose the Catholics or the fags or the Jews. Makes no difference."

I told him that I did not think that was entirely true, I thought it was the racism in the American character that was at cause.

"Racism? It's *hate*, baby. Hate. Like in France under the Catholic kings, no blacks around, it was the Protestants who were niggers. In England the Catholics, in Russia the liberals, in Spain the Protestants again, and in Egypt the Jews, in Israel the Arabs, in the Congo the whites. Just good old human hate. That's the enemy. They gotta pay. And, baby, when you make hate *rich*, why there's no end to the niggers you can find with all that middle-class American leisure on your hands. The fags and dykes and hippies and the young... Jesus! No *end* to it."

I went home with him that night. A white stone building,

formerly a town house, stricken by age and speculation, the carved oak walls painted over and over, everything a shrill white or institutional green. Dim lighting. Disinfectant. The place smelling like prisons I have smelled. Al's building for once was not owned by Columbia (it was owned by some Jewish slumlord who lived on the East Side and wintered in Miami Beach) but it had the characteristics of the depressing dumps Columbia maintains at a profit for her sons.

He had one large room on the fourth floor for which he paid a hundred and twenty-five bills a month. A fireplace (non-working), one very large mattress on the floor, a couple of chairs, a desk, an old sofa, a kitchenette, a bath. And on the walls pictures of the Saints: Che, Fidel, Camus, Malcolm X. And the Devil: a dart board with the face of Mighty Lyndon, the Wizard, pasted on.

Jerry, his roommate, was wearing a terrycloth mini-robe. "Come on in, Honey," he said, opening the door and giving me a wide, wide, Idaho, countryboy, roll-me-in-the-hay smile. He was beautiful. The two boys kissed and Al swatted Jerry on the butt and told him to get the stud (meaning himself) and skinny (meaning me) some drinks. Jerry wandered off toward the kitchenette unhappily, pissed at having to play Cinderella before the Gentleman Caller.

"A hole, right?" Al asked me, glancing around his room. I nodded that it was.

"Then you should see where my old lady lives, baby, 121st Street, East Harlem, surrounded by spics who can't speak the language and goddamn junkies who won't, working in a goddamn laundromat for some Jew-kike and forever paying off payments on a lot of crap furniture no respectable honkey would give to a goddamn thrift shop. Man, it is one pain in the ass being a nigger in your country."

Jerry returned with the drinks. He gave me mine and handed Al's to him, kissing him as he did. Al and I were standing. Jerry sat down on the sofa, looking up at me very

53

innocently as he did, letting his mini-robe fall off his thighs showing me his equipment.

Al caught his gesture and laughed at its obviousness. "Okay, babe, show time's over. Get into the goddamn bed."

"I'm not tired!"

"To bed! The men want to talk and you're distracting us." He certainly was distracting.

"The men!" he snorted, getting up and making a little swish walk over to the mattress, I catching a glimpse of his strong, outdoor shoulders and legs as he fell on his stomach letting his robe slip halfway up his butt. "The men! Ha!"

Al walked over to the mattress and knelt down, glancing self-consciously, charmingly up at me as he did, kissed his kid and then threw a blanket over him. He turned off all the lights but the one by the sofa and came over and sat down by me.

"Has to get up in the morning," he said softly. "He's trying to be a model and so he has to make the rounds. Got to look pretty," he said proudly, glancing over at Jerry lying Lana Turneresque on the mattress.

"He ought to be big someday," I remarked.

"He'll be big, baby, so big he can't afford me."

From the bed: "I'll never leave you, Al."

"Sure, kid. But when you do, remember you owe this black boy four months back rent."

Al and I sat up the night talking about SAS and about what a waste of time he thought the Student Afro-American Society was. "The only thing those cats do is publish a crummy magazine once in awhile and talk about black nationalism and black self-help, try to come off as white as possible."

I asked him why he had come to Columbia. "I don't know. To be near the old lady . . . and then, you know, taking the train by those damn gates for years, never thinking I could get in . . . that was before the Ivy League went Tokenism and

54

decided they needed you even if you couldn't get into City College. But maybe I shouldn't have. Sometimes I think the life's in the streets, in our city, Harlem. *Only* there, with the losers. The only thing Columbia's good for is becoming an Uncle Tom and getting a job with the Urban League. For *that* you need a degree. But you don't need it for anything else, nothing important. Not for revolution. . . . And, baby, I'm going to make the motherfuckers pay, the rich bastards who bleed Harlem and make money off of wars, the self-righteous who've hurt the kid [he indicated Jerry, but I think he meant himself]. Those Idaho pricks . . . they practically rode him out of the state on a rail because he's gay. Sick. The fucking country is so fucking sick! Why, shit, why do they love to beat us down? The bastards! It makes no sense."

Al told me the discomfort he felt in being at Columbia, the petty ways in which the University made him feel unwanted, there at whitey's sufferance.

"Ever been to a Barnard mixer?" I nodded that I had. "Well, go in black face sometime. Man, I went to one the first week I was on campus. I like girls, breaks the monotony. . . ." He laughed, his shoulders shaking, handsomely. "And I made the mistake of going early. And there is some damn old lady bitch, from the Dean's Office or something, and she says to me, she says, 'Boy,' that's what she says, 'Boy, the tables are set up. You better get one of those white serving coats over there, otherwise you might spill the punch on your clothes.' The bitch thought I was a servant, she couldn't imagine a black boy coming as a guest. And let me tell you something else, nearly every night when I'm on campus and go into one of the dorms, nearly every goddamn night some motherfucking security man, and he's *black*, too, the bugger, asks to see my I.D., like I'm some neighborhood jerk come to steal the rugs. Never asks none of the whites, no sir, just the black students. Great place, Columbia." Al continued, his anger stiffening in recall, "One of these sweet times those

55

bastards are going to push me too far.... When Jimmy, he's another black, got into his dorm his two lily-white roommates in New Hall asked to be transferred out. He transferred out instead, into Livingston. Columbia's Southern, not only in the way it treats Harlem, that's nothing new, but in the way they treat *us*. They *invite* us there, for Christ's sake, and then act like we're a bunch of nigger rapists. Why have us in in the first place? Shit, the whole country's racist-Southern, full of Southern hate, from one fucking shore to the other, they're all rednecks and Bull Connors, every last one of them. Hate. The national pastime.... And you know something...?"

"What?"

"You know why I like fags, should I tell you why I like the gay community? Because, baby, they don't *care* what goddamn color you are. They only discriminate in sex. Period. That's where it ends. And I tell you it's a *relief* to know the only thing a crowd of people at a party or a bar look at's your basket. That's a relief. You can get by then. That's fair. That's human, man, that's real. The rest of it, these liberals crying about poor darkie we got to get into old Columbia, yeah, like they want to put you on a shelf and buy off Harlem and their fucking liberal consciences with your black body. That's what they want to do."

When I left I asked Al to meet me the next day after work. I wanted him to see a Warhol movie about a hustler that had opened on 44th Street.

"Maybe. Yeah, why not?"

He walked me into the hall and said, perhaps to explain what I already knew, "Dotson, I let you in on a secret. Even if I wasn't gay I'd fuck that white boy in there. 'Cause, man, when we're making it he don't care if I'm green or pink or what. It's *me* he wants. Me! And, God, how I need that, how I need that kid to want *me*."

Stating the obvious, I said, "You're lucky to have him, Al."

He smiled, or rather he *beamed* with delight. "Oh, man, you don't *know* how lucky, you don't know!"

By the first week of October everyone was back in town, in school, and the rhythm began again. I registered for Lionel Trilling's course on Modern Literature and Daniel Dodson's course on the drama and fell in love with language and myth again and realized how easily, over one summer, I could grow to miss the books and students and teachers and the pattern of loneliness and defiance that characterized student life at Columbia.

By the beginning of the term we were becoming increasingly aware of our disaffection from the University. With the SDS demonstrations late the semester before against Marine recruiting on campus, and with the first charges of the University's official ties with defense research directly related to the war in Vietnam and, just beginning, the questioning of the University's decision to construct a new College gymnasium on public lands in Morningside Park ("Harlem's Park")—tired of being disregarded, the war escalating, fierce, senseless, students already pulled from classes and taken to military camps, we began to sense acutely our loneliness at Columbia. Our university. Undergraduate housing bleak and unfriendly. A surly, unresponsive bureaucracy. An administration defensive, closed-mouthed, hidden like thieves in Low Library, aloof, imperially indifferent (Forever Mr. Big: Kirk, "I'm a very busy man!" Humpf, humpf!) to its faculty and students. Mark Rudd, then simply one member of SDS, said, "Someday we'll win when we make that bastard [President Kirk] stay after five o'clock because his students need attention." Rudd. Moderate then. We all were. Loneliness, the feeling of isolation, of being discounted, feeding defiance. That fall.

I remember going to see Trilling a couple of afternoons early in the term—busy man, short office hours, his heart there and open, fatigued, impotent as we, sensing the disaffection and the anger, unable to help—and telling him about a friend of mine in need of help, wanting to die, on scholarship, having no money, and his going to what the College laughingly termed its "Counseling Service" and being referred to Saint Luke's, getting his three fifty-minute sessions with the overburdened, underpaid staff psychiatrist, and then being told to seek private help. He had used up his budgeted time with the head shrinker. He had to pay for further help by himself (Dean Truman, when asked at a Fireside Chat why Columbia did not have as extensive a psychiatric service as Harvard, replied, "We're not in the business of running a mental hospital, we're in the business of teaching." How true). And Trilling asked what the boy needed, what could he do to help.

I told Mr. Trilling that the boy needed the same thing nearly every other underclassman needed. He needed to be listened to. Away from home, living in one of the grim Columbia beehives, forced, from a lack of coins, to eat twice a day everyday but Sunday in one of the campus eating halls (that, dear friend, is cruel and unusual punishment), knowing few people, having no bread to take a girl out on a decent date (and Barnard girls, thinking our Sister School is an uptown Miss Porter's, define "decent date" at around thirty bucks, dinner and a show, just like in Stamford). Generally fucked up. Confined. And why is it the University's responsibility that some of its sons kill themselves and drop out and drift into acid and speed and hustling and, unlucky ones, the twilight hell: Needle Park, Inc. Because the anguish appears while they are there, on campus, away from home. I told Trilling that I did not believe that Kirk or Dean Truman (later Vice President) realized the delicacy of young men, the ease with which they are wounded and put off, their need to have their personhood affirmed. Daily. Seventeen. Eighteen. Nineteen years of age. Men, real, live, honest to God, potent men. Able to father kids, by jingo, to do meaningful work even, to die at a President's whim, simply, obscurely, gratuitously, unasked, unvoting, kept in a prolonged adolescence (holds down the sexual and job competition), exploited.

One afternoon I walked Trilling to his office from class. And going into Hamilton Hall he pointed to the handles on the doors. "Look at those handles. Not the same size at all. Unbalanced. The whole place is like that."

Upstairs, sitting in the armchair across from his desk, the walls lined with books, ESTABLISHMENT, POSITION, written beyond contradiction in every gesture, every line; white-haired, sly-humored, Sophistication like a religious calling, intimidating, strong, uncomfortable with his compassion. I sat across from him and complained about the University, about my sex life, about how badly things were going, about his class (Trilling seemed to have a peculiar effect on me. In his presence I was never more foul-mouthed, never lonelier, never so in need of confirmation. Surrogate father to the pack of us) while he chain-smoked and thrust back boredom and supported that crooked, interested smile. Beautiful man. He worried about us, or at least he appeared to worry. He had a son of our generation. He worried.

During the first week of the semester I had drinks with Professor Dodson, in the Men's Faculty Club, no less (You're A Big Boy Now, Charlie Brown). We talked about writing and about the School of General Studies and how the faculty there, like the entire faculty, was getting the well-aimed shaft from the Pontifical Mr. Kirk. We talked about the radical students on campus. Even the faculty had begun to listen.

When I mentioned the U.N. march to him and told him about the beating I had seen, he asked if I had had enough of protest. I said No, I thought it was only beginning.

"Then you are going to Washington for the March?" he

asked, drinking another scotch and soda, his eyes hazed, his mind drifting back to ... to what? Being eighteen in Austria when the *Anschluss* hit with lightning, the fighting in the streets, the underground Resistance, hopeless with the Nazi police already rounding up his friends, one of them to end in Dachau; being young and radical in the late Thirties and comparing himself to us. Don't be good Germans over Vietnam, he advised, stand up to the bastards. Replay the Resistance and the truth.

"What march?" I asked, reading the papers seldom.

"Dave Dellinger is having another march. Against the Pentagon, I guess. The Mobilization Committee ... My daughter's going."

"Sure, I'll go. Why not?"

"Do you think there'll be violence?" he asked, thinking of his daughter. "It's supposed to be a big march, the Committee expects about a half a million protesters." Half a million. Jesus!

No, I did not think there would be violence. One never thought there would be violence. Then, months from the U.N. bust, my outrage had filtered into detachment, my ethics into a private fear.

"I was at King's march in '63," I said. "There wasn't any violence then." Not that day, the Showman's last spectacular, the final, lovely, sparkling minstrel show the old Baptist staged, his pulpit marble and windblown before the figure of the forlorn Lincoln. I HAVE A DREAM! Voice quivering, loving it, high with its sound. I HAVE A DREAM! And that was what it was, nothing more. The Bill was passed. And while it did no harm, Brother King got what he thought his people wanted. A Civil Rights Bill to end all Civil Rights Bills.

"The King march got the Bill passed. Perhaps ... if this is as big ... perhaps King Lyndon will listen. What do you think?"

Professor Dodson shrugged. "Who knows? It's worth a try, at least it's worth a try."

A few days later Sophie called. She and her new boyfriend, Saul, had decided to go to the March. "Dotson, *wait* until you see this number. Honey, he ain't goy, that's for damn sure, one of the tribe, but is he hung and big and, really, Dotson, now don't laugh, really, I really think he loves me!" A long pause while she waited for a suitable response from me. I was woefully unimpressed. "About time, I should think," she said defensively, "after the grief I upped with the likes of schmucks like you!" She went on and finally got around to asking me if I would come along. I said Yes. Later we talked Sean into driving and asked Al along, too.

Friday, in order to make sure that Sean got up by five, I went down to the East Village where he lived and stayed the night. Sean's apartment was one large room with bricked-up windows to keep thieves out, a bathtub by the "kitchen" sink, and cockroaches—unbelievably bold—everywhere. A bathroom in the hall with a hole in the ceiling, as big as the Ritz, wide enough to see into the bathroom above. Sean was a senior at Columbia and why the hell he lived in that sty I will never know. It had something to do with the same kind of identification with the poor that Rachel had. Like hers it was clean and self-defeating.

The next morning, Saturday, October 21, we piled into Sean's car and drove to Washington. I tried to sleep in the front seat, with Al squashed between Sean and me, while Sophie and Saul, their sex receiving a certain kick out of being performed behind the backs of three sex-starved young men, played the fuck for all it was worth in the back seat. It would be costly. Once we reached the Pentagon the two exercised lovers would fall asleep on the mall while the rest of us acted out our dark beads with the troops.

Washington, as has often been remarked, is at heart a

small Southern town. When we drove into Freedom City the place was crawling with cops and troopers, the White House was surrounded by guards, its sidewalk closed by a long, steel cable fence. No one on the streets, no one straight, that is, the office workers were out of sight, the politicians hiding behind drawn shades, the blacks cramped safely in their sprawling ghettos. Only the cops and us.

We parked the car by the canal in Georgetown and walked around looking for a place to eat. The first place we tried was run by some Georgia cracker and he, seeing Saul's hair and Sophie's clothes (a small Vietnam/Vietcong flag pinned to her dress) and my buttons and Sean's poster ("Johnson and Humphrey Are Queer For War") and Al's color decided he could not find us a table in his near-empty café. We left, after putting up an appropriate bitch and calling him a Communist (Why "Communist" I do not know, except it struck us as the term which would drive him out of his bird. "You dirty Communist shopkeeper!").

We ended up at Howard Johnson's, where all the food the pieman serves tastes the same, and had ourselves overdone hamburgers.

Then we walked past the Treasury Building in the hot sun and over to the Washington Monument and to the approach to Lincoln Memorial. It was about one o'clock when we arrived. The area on either side of the reflecting pool, from the Memorial to the road behind the fountains at the end of the pool, from there all the way to the Monument steps, was filled with protesters. Of every variety. Everyone was in a good mood. A picnic on Saturday afternoon. Vietcong flags, American flags, banners, posters, Guerilla Theatre.

"Let's move up front, by the pool, where we can see," Al suggested. Sophie objected. She wanted to go under the trees with her Mr. America-built man and sleep the sleep of the just.

We moved forward and sat near the front, far from where

62

Mailer had begun to grandstand, from Lowell and Raskin and MacDonald and the other Notables in front and above us. We sat by the edge of the pool. I took off my shoes and dangled my feet in the water as Dr. Spock said, "We are convinced that this war which Lyndon Johnson is waging is disastrous to our country in every way, and that we, the protesters, are the ones who may help to save our country if we can persuade our fellow citizens to think and vote as we do." Spock continued in his middle-aged way stating the failure of democracy, "The enemy is Lyndon Johnson, whom we elected as a peace candidate in 1964 and who betrayed us within three months, who has stubbornly led us deeper and deeper into a bloody quagmire in which uncounted hundreds of thousands of Vietnamese . . . have died and thirteen thousand young Americans, too."

The sun was blinding, my contact lenses were hurting me, my eyes watering. Al lay down beside me and put his head on my lap, a handkerchief over his eyes, and lay there dallying his long fingers in the water, his black face handsome against the whiteness of my pants. His gesture unnerved me at first, but after awhile I thought, who the hell cares? I wondered what Al was thinking as he lay there listening to the speeches in the hot sun, I wondered if like me he began to wonder exactly what Dellinger had meant by going from demonstration to resistance, what precise acts of civil disobedience would be attempted, what it meant to *seek* confrontation with Federal troops.

Sophie and Saul slept uncomfortably, waking every twenty minutes or so to annoy the people around them, changing positions, stretching their feet out into the backs of the people in front. Every once in awhile they would wake and feel each other out, kiss, press the flesh, glance around to see who was watching and then, Sophie assured that her sexual attractiveness had been made visible to the entire world, to Al and me in particular, the two lovers would drift back into sleep

(Sophie looked good that day. Her hair straight and short as usual, but she was wearing a definitely *feminine* dress and no bra, allowing her large breasts to fall and move and impress). Sean went off in search of the Columbia contingent, leaving the four of us to bake in the sun.

The speeches were a bore. At times embarrassing. Especially the little number the sister of Malcolm X unloaded. Her anger unbalanced her. The two genuinely moving moments, when the blood heated and we realized why we were there and whom we hated, came when the Abraham Lincoln Brigade, which had fought the fascists in the Spanish Civil War, came hobbling through the crowd and we stood to our feet, ignoring the speakers on the platform, and in one body applauded what was there they symbolized of our fathers' generation which touched our hearts. Aging, some limping, few in number, they made their way through the throng, heads high, proudly, reminding me of nothing so much as World War One veterans that one sees occasionally in Independence Day parades, their war over, Madrid fallen, like nice guys everywhere finishing last. In that moment the solidarity with the Left I experienced at the U.N. returned and suddenly I was proud of us, the outrage returned and with it—and with Phil Ochs' lament "The War Is Over"—the utter absurdity of our gesture came over me. The government's response to our petition, even before the March began, before the petition was offered, was evidenced by the troopers lining the city, the machine guns nested on the Pentagon roof, the police helicopters fluttering above. Impotent we were. Again. The President would not listen. No one with power would. We counted for nothing. We were worth simply the cost of the troops and the tear gas it would take to break us down. No more.

Again the passion swelled when Phil Ochs sang, *I declare the war is over, it's over, it's over....* Al looked up at me from my pillowed lap and, covering his eyes from the sun with his hand, his smile wide, "Baby, listen to that *beau*tiful cat sing!

Baby, just you listen!" *So do your duty, boys, and join the crowd; serve your country, enter suicide; find a flag so you can wave good-bye, but just before the end even treason might be worth a try . . . this country is too young to die . . . I declare the war is over. . . .* And it came up and over me what would confront me again and again; sitting there with that black boy's head cupped in the hollow of my thighs, his body tumbling softly with the singer's beat, Lincoln in marble, shielded and brooding beneath the columns to the left of which a National Liberation flag flapped, to the west of which Fortress Pentagon tightened itself with its troops, the American government defending itself from the American people . . . *even treason might be worth a try, this country is too young to die* . . . loving the young and new Left, the sheer waste of their guts, the absurdity of their song, the inability of America to let us be free . . . free, to be free. I thought of 1963 and King, dead now, crossed over, and how different his march had been. Even Congress showed to collect television points, sitting like French whores on the steps of the Lincoln Memorial while King wailed his dream and we shouted PASS THE BILL! PASS THE BILL! They passed it. But three years later we were beyond bills and, although we did not really know it, beyond reunion and faith, on the borders of violence and soon with the troopers and guns, we would be again beyond loyalty. One thought reoccurred many times to me: It is my country. It is my land. Mine! Who the hell do those motherfuckers think they are with their guns and bayonets and gas bombs? So different from the U.N. bust. Here the obscenity was made in the symbols of American democracy. The troopers lacked the human sense that New York's cops have even at their most vicious. The cops get off their cookies beating the kids. But here, the Army! The Corps of Engineers! Planned, cold, distant, vulgar and foreign in Washington. Unreal. Christ, it blew the mind like some kind of It Can't Happen Here nightmare.

It was middle afternoon before the line of march began its slow progress across the Potomac bridge, Mailer and the stars leading us. When Sean returned, he and Al and I left the two lovers on the grass and wormed our way through various parade contingents to the front sections of the line of march. There we were told to link arms. We did. And we sang marching across the bridge, hot, happy, as usual thinking we were actually accomplishing something politically significant.

On the Virginia side of the Potomac. The line of march spread out and the marchers ambled toward the Pentagon, walking past a sewage station fenced and troop-guarded to prevent us from doing what? Swimming? Past groups of troops and police, under highway bridges lined with high school boys waving American flags and shouting, END THE WAR! through the long grass of the meadows toward the parking lots where the Pentagon rally was to be held. The near approaches to the building (the largest in the world, with ugliness on a scale to match) were closed with snow fences and steel link fences and three columns of very young soldiers from Fort Bragg and Fort Belvoir and Fort Dix and Fort Meade and Fort Eustis and Fort Hood. On the far corner of the parking lot a group of heads gathered chanting, hoping to levitate the Pentagon. The speeches began. Most of the young people (and of the quarter of a million who marched, most were young) disregarded the speeches and moved on to the fences.

The three of us stood in the tall grass before the knoll and bushes that separated the Pentagon mall from the parking lot. Southwest the building loomed gray and massive, tiny, doll-like figures pacing beweaponed on its vast roof. Suddenly to our left there was a great deal of noise. We turned and looked as thousands of people began to break from the parking lots and rush on to the mall. Trotskyites—always the vanguard —had broken through the snow fences and police lines and had made it to the mall. After the initial break and a few arrests the troops moved back. The mall was ours.

Al, Sean and I ran with the crowd toward the Pentagon terrace and there, jammed with other young people, we pressed against the troops and shouted END THE WAR! BRING THE TROOPS HOME! That went on all afternoon. Every once in a while someone in front would be pushed too close to a marshal (and the Federal marshals, in terms of my experience, are beyond doubt the cruelest of police) and he would bring his club down and the person would scream and the young troops near would wince involuntarily and the lines would tighten and the poor bastard be dragged away by the marshals, his head being clubbed as he neared the police vans.

The afternoon wore on. The crowd of protesters on the mall increased in size, dividing itself into three loose contingents, one of which held the terrace and pressed against the troops before the building, and the two others which moved on either side of the mall, one pushing and withdrawing and pushing again against the troop lines guarding the access road to the River Entrance of the Pentagon, the other, farther west, moving against the marshals and troops on the other side. Al, Sean and I played the mall, running from one side to the other, joining bands of young men who attempted occasional penetrations of the troop lines, shouting End The War! laughing, catching glimpses of McNamara and the Generals at the windows, raising our fingers in a V-salute, laughing. None of us had ever been at the Pentagon before. It made you high dancing on the grass, natant with the tension, the sheer joy of being where the military did not want you to be, running now and again when the troops, ordered by their superiors to amuse the watching Mr. McNamara with a show of force, would rush out boldly, awkwardly in little groups into the crowd and attempt to push the protesters back. Young soldiers. Their hearts were not really in it. They could not muster up the necessary contempt to be effective.

They would break ranks and move into the crowd, taking their rifles and pushing against us trying to force us back. We would give way and retreat into the mall, the few troops moving with us, and then, with the troops isolated from their companies, we would surround them, split them from each other, escort them up the terrace ramps, remove their helmets, rifles and clubs and send the weapons flying through the air.

As night fell and more of us were arrested—over four hundred that afternoon—and as the marshals became bolder and harder in their violence, as it darkened and the temperature cooled, dampened, the wind rising, we grew sober and anxious, the tension mounting. Our numbers decreased. Mailer was arrested. Lowell and the other stars went home. The press began to slip away. The protesters diminished to less than a thousand. Anonymous. Unarmed. Finally outnumbered by the watching troops. Most of us gathered on the terrace (it was filthy with ash, spilled paint, blood, urine, soda, papers, cups, discarded clothing, broken sticks) and lit bonfires there and on the mall (using the wood from the snow fences originally put up to keep us away). We sang. We talked. We boasted. We strutted. Someone came with a box of ham and cheese sandwiches. Blankets were handed around. A couple near the ramp wall of the terrace, several feet before the troop line, put blankets down and made love. We heard the rumor that the troops would bust us at midnight, when the permit allegedly expired. We had waited for hours. It was good to learn it would end. The tension. We would be prepared.

I asked Sean and Al if they wanted to leave before the midnight deadline. Al said, "Now how can we, man, how can we when all the sell-outs have left? We're the *people*, the Movement, if we go, Jesus, just because of the chance that we might get arrested then we'll never stay, ever, for anything. Then we'll always run."

I told him that it was not the fact of arrest that bothered me but the possibility of violence. Some of the protesters had

68

already attempted to provoke bloodshed and by midnight, with most of the press gone, I did not think the troops would hesitate to beat the hell out of us once our legal right to assemble was lifted.

"Shit, Dotson," Al said, "blood's part of the game. There's a cost to everything." And Sean supported Al, adding that the *number* of arrests were important. I agreed to stay until after midnight, although I was cold and admittedly frightened and had no stomach for swinging rifle butts.

About ten-thirty Sophie and Saul wandered up to the terrace. They were bored and tired. Saul said we could stay overnight at a friend's house in Washington. They would meet us at the car in Georgetown if we were not arrested. If we were, they would try to get us bail. They left.

The next two hours passed quickly. The three of us sat on blankets, with our backs to a small fire, facing the troops. We talked to them about the war (I spoke incessantly, almost hysterically, babbled about the war and sex and politics and death; I shivered like I had Parkinson's Disease, the cold and hunger and the fear making me shake. It was embarrassing). We sang, *before I'll be a slave I'll be buried in my grave and go home to my Lord and be free. . . .* And *I'm gonna lay down my napalm bomb* [boom-boom] *down by the riverside* [boom-boom] *down by the riverside . . . ain'a gonna study war no more. . . .* There were lights on in many of the Pentagon windows, guard lights on outside, light from the fires playing on the faces of the young soldiers standing rigidly before us, inches away in two straight, tight lines, eyes focused directly ahead, the irises mirroring the fires, looking sad and uncomfortable.

During the afternoon four of the troops had deserted their posts and joined the protesters and we hoped for more defections.

"Man, don't you know what you're doing here?" Al preached, standing on the blanket. I sat at his left side and looked up at him, his dark face shiny in the light, his eyes seeming unnaturally large and beautiful. "We're Americans, too, you know, we haven't done nothing and we aren't going to, brother, except to try and stop this fascist, imperialist war. Listen, soldier, they got you in an Army and they filling your head with a lot of crap about Nation Building in Southeast Asia and Defending Democracy. Who's going to build *this* nation, stop the poverty and the killing here? Who's going to defend democracy here against King Lyndon and the Texas boys? Huh? Who, if you and me don't, baby? If you don't come on our side? You *need* that gun, that bayonet, that knife? To protect yourself from *us?* Do you really?"

Midnight came. No arrests. We were told that the permit was legitimate through Sunday. Some of the protesters left. Several hundred stayed through until morning.

As Al, Sean and I walked away from the terrace Sean turned to me and said, "It looks like a Displaced Person's camp, remember? Like those pictures of Spain during the Civil War with the refugees camped at night in town squares before government buildings?" Before us the mall was dotted by a dozen small fires, each surrounded by a group of young people maintaining their vigil before the War Building. The night was cool, the wind was up, you could smell the Potomac water and the grass and you could hear, attenuated, stanzas muffled by the wind, phrases of folk songs, laughter, talk. Over the trees across the water the Washington Monument.

We walked across the mall to the road beyond the small knoll and bushes leading to the River Entrance of the Pentagon where a number of marshals stood silently, clubs gripped between their two hands, some smoking, unsmiling, suspicious, glaring at us as we moved toward the parking lots.

By a small grove of trees near the road, hedged by bushes, Al took a piss and the sound of his water made me want to go. We stood together in the bushes, the only sound the noise of our water hitting the leaves and the dim, thin chatter and singing of the youth on the mall and the fading roar of a airplane overhead. As we pissed, Al said to me, "I'm lonely." He said it very softly.

"Why?"

"I don't know."

"For what?"

"Don't know that either," he said, both of us finishing and moving out away from the bushes toward the road. "Maybe for Jerry . . . for Godot," he laughed at the academic image. "Christ, I don't know. For someone."

We stood on the road several paces from the rope strung across the upper section of the pavement behind which the marshals stood. Sean and I lit cigarettes. "Look at the mother-fuckers," Al said, indicating the marshals. As we smoked he walked alone closer to the rope. Then he shouted, "You motherfucking redneck marshals! You fascist bastards! You honkey racist pigs!" Shouted or howled or groaned it. His anger was chilling, catching us by surprise, fierce, so unlike Al, foreign to him as I knew him.

"Al!" I called, "Shut up! You'll get our ass in trouble!"

Sean and I stood on the road by the trees in the shadows and called to Al. He would not listen. He walked quickly away from us toward the marshals with his hands raised high in the air, his fists clenched, shouting, "Motherfucking fascist pigs!" He trotted to the rope behind which the marshals stood unmoving, braced, watching him. Three of them, middle-aged, dressed in business suits and motorcycle helmets, whitemen. "Al!" Sean yelled and started to run toward him. I went after Sean and grabbed him from behind. "Al, don't!" he shouted, as I held him tightly. It was not our time, it was his. What he did seemed senseless and futile and defeatist, yet it was his thing. And I felt, I think almost instinctively, that to interfere physically, to attempt to prevent him from confronting the marshals (and God only knows what they stood for in his mind which he needed to face), to interdict his act at that point would have been to humiliate him. To lose him. That I could not do.

While the marshals stood unmoving, Al darted under the rope and made a quick dash to the left, dodging by them, and ran up the road toward the River Entrance. He disappeared in the darkness and in the noise of the marshals shouting ahead to stop the black bastard from making it to the doors.

Sean and I stood there a moment stunned. I looked at Sean. "What the hell?" I said. We waited. Then we walked on.

chapter five

IT IS ONE HELL OF A LONG WALK FROM THE PENTA-gon to Georgetown. It seems longer at night. Especially when you have spent nearly a day and a night protesting and running, tense, worn through. One hell of a walk. What happened to Al silenced Sean and me. We walked through the parking lots at the Pentagon and then into the meadows and to the Potomac bridge, Arlington National Cemetery backing up behind us, John F. Kennedy's flame flickering on the hillside beneath the Custis-Lee Mansion. The bridge empty of traffic. Cops sitting in patrol cars along the way ignoring us. I felt lonely, wanting to hold someone, missing Al strangely, remembering the outline of his face as he preached to the troops.

We crossed the bridge. We walked to Pennsylvania Avenue and along it past the White House, dark, the fountain lit and falling, the grounds still guarded by police in helmets and boots. We sat in Lafayette Park across from the White House, on a bench by a bed of flowers, our backs to the Mansion, the gold dome of St. John's Church glinting under the street lamp in front of us. There were three sailors cruising in the park and a black couple lying on the grass under a tulip tree asleep.

"I'm tired," I said to Sean.

"So am I." He lit a cigarette, the last one he had, and we both shared it.

As we got up to leave he said, "I wonder how Al is. I wonder if they hurt him bad."

We walked past George Washington University and into Georgetown. We found the car. A note left by Sophie gave us the address of the house where we were to stay. We stepped into the car and drove to I Street.

Sean and I slept in a double bed in the basement. The walls were knotty pine. The furnace was on. It was warm. We slept like logs. Dead the minute we hit the sack.

"Rise and shine! Another day, another dollar!" Sophie said, coming into the basement shaking us awake. It was about eleven o'clock.

"Morning, Sophie," I said, and then rolled over. I had forgotten I was in Washington. For some reason I was under the firm impression that I was asleep in New York.

"Come on, you bum. Eleven o'clock you sleep in the morning like this is day camp. Mr. Waldorf-Astoria with nothing to do. Have you seen the newspapers this hick town calls *news*papers? Oy! What that ass Breslin says about us? Up! Read!"

I sat up. She dropped *The Washington Post* on my lap. She went upstairs.

Sean and I read the Sunday papers in bed, angry at what we believed was misrepresentation of the march, angrier still at Jimmy Breslin's snide, phony-Hemingway remarks about unwashed protesters. "That jerk!" Sean said, reading his column, "that arrogant jerk. He thinks like a blue collar worker only he ain't one. He slums, the dumb Mick."

Upstairs. We sat down at the table. Eggs. Bacon. Toast. Coffee. My head hurt, like a hangover, and I was depressed wondering why the hell we had come in the first place, what good did it ever do? We were never listened to, not as long as they had the troops and the press and the government. Maybe arms were needed. Treason? Why not? How does the victim betray his jailer? I was in a romantically depressed state.

Sophie asked, "Where's your friend, Al? He stay the night in the War Room?" Then I remembered.

The man in whose house we were staying (a Federal worker in the Navy Department, no less) called the police and then the Mobilization Committee and located the probable whereabouts of Al. He was in jail in Virginia. He was to be released at noon. No, we could not contact him. Yes, he had transportation back to New York. No, as far as they knew he suffered no injury.

I felt good with Al safe. I wanted to get to the Pentagon for more.

We drove to the Lincoln Memorial and parked the car. There were half a hundred protesters sitting on the steps of the Memorial in the sun waiting to form a contingent to march together to the Pentagon to join the people who had stayed the night.

Sophie and Saul sat down on the lower steps of the Memorial by a group of students from Dartmouth ("Dartmouth Fucks The War!"). Sophie flirted with the boys. By that I mean that she sprawled on the steps, eyed the boys, slapped them on the thigh, kissed Saul deeply, stopped, looked around for appreciative reaction, mumbled obscenities against Johnson, Humphrey and McNamara, kissed again, generally put on a public display. Sean and I climbed the steps and entered the Memorial itself. Stood awhile before the Lincoln statue. Read the words engraved on the walls. Grew quiet.

As we walked down the steps Sean said, "This war is horrible . . . not just because of the soldiers and civilians dying, not because of the money wasted. You know, it is so goddamn horrible because it is so *American,* really, for the first time, a war that *fits* what America has become, what she is. We're nothing like Lincoln's America, different in *kind*. I think America loves war. She loves to kill . . . guns, weapons, beating young people, dropping tons of bombs on people you never see. She gets a charge out of it . . . sick. She is sick."

I left Sean with Sophie and Saul and went in search of a bathroom (I knew we would be leaving for the Pentagon and so at that moment, just like at every other time when I am nervous about something about to begin, my bladder presses. Billy Graham once told me he always took a piss before he preached to a Crusade crowd. I know why). I discovered the men's room hidden behind evergreen bushes, the doorway to the side of the steps in the foundation of the Memorial.

I went inside. There were three black kids, about five years of age, swinging on the doors of the toilet stalls.

"You got a dime, mister?" one of the boys yelled from his swinging perch.

I gave them a quarter. They squealed and went tearing out of the men's room delighted with their good fortune. As I walked over to the urinals I noticed a young man, maybe seventeen years old, standing facing the urinals. He had long, black hair, dark eyes. He was thin, small, boyish, dressed in a sport shirt, a cardigan sweater, and brown pants. I remember him vividly. He wore a peace button pinned to his shirt below his collar. I went up to one of the urinals (there were three and each of us stood at a urinal at either end with the middle one between us). I started to urinate. He coughed. Twice. I looked over. He was standing about a foot away from the edge of his urinal, his back very straight, his groin forward, his legs bent slightly at the knee, holding his erect penis in his hand, looking down at himself with his black hair falling in a lock over his eyes. Oh, Christ, I thought, to get cornered with a faggot. When I glanced over at him he looked up and attempted a smile. I do not know why—whether it was guilt

76

coming from my failure to respond to the need of a homosexual, a friend, Al, the night before, whether it was fatigue—
but I felt immense pity for the boy, so great that I felt suddenly near tears as he stood holding his organ and swiveled
slowly until he was facing me, a kind of shy artifice, a grace-
fulness to his movement. There was something desperate in
his gesture, lonely, twisted, forlorn (I thought of a party I had
attended weeks before given by an Underground film-maker
where his Superstars came in drag on a Queens' Night, hysteric, losers, and postured at love and sex, grotesque camp,
sad, and I was impressed by the conventionality of my mind
in that situation, how straight I was in reaction, judgmental,
with painted victims the middle-class normalness, almost Cal-
vinistic, of my response to human feelings, how I, inspite of
loud complaint, had made it thus far through life without
suffering irreparably their anguish and loss) yet somehow
connected critically with the perversion of values, the atrophy
of human sentiment which the war symbolized. All he said
was "please." I said nothing. His gesture frightened me. Good
God, are there not enough taxes made upon our body of
compassion without this insistent demand by those eyes
(young. Christ, open. I will not forget) on me. He offered in
the most primitive way human contact, a kind of affirmation
that has grown poor and discredited in America. All night
before those young troops, hundreds arrested, beatings, Al
rushing and taken, and the mind is unbalanced. Unreal to
walk in the darkness from the fortified Pentagon, alien in my
land, past the Kennedy flame, exiled in heart, the threads
severed by the possibility of violence everywhere (Was there
ever a time in America when the young did not confront in
daylight with each political act the threat of violence? Was
there ever a time?) and then, unrecovered, to be faced with
that boy who had probably sat the night through on the terrace—like me wishing the tension, almost sexual in demand,
would break, one way or another, through our violence or

theirs, if only to come to a goddamn end—to be faced by his hard penis and need. It exhausted me. Fragmented, foreign yet real, unexpected/unwanted yet there, personal as a private fear (later, when the Columbia rebellion came I left one afternoon and went to John Jay Hall and in the bathroom was confronted again in a kind of déja vu by a similar young man with a similar need, but a young man I knew, a radical student I never suspected of intrasexuality; he, too, said "please") and it was interwound with the attack on manhood, the death-in-life that the war and riots and escalating violence had directed against young manhood. A moment after he turned I left. Jesus God Almighty how lonely must you be to posit love in a public urinal?

We walked to the Pentagon. Sophie had a lunch basket. We sat on the grass under the trees and ate sandwiches and drank cheap red wine. Then we went up again to the terrace and talked to the troops and the protesters.

At dusk Saul walked back to the Lincoln Memorial and picked up the car. We met him on the bridge. We piled into the car. On the other side of the bridge a protester was standing with a great deal of rope coiled around his chest, bags and boxes piled on the road beside him. Sophie saw him, recognizing him. "Hey, stop! That's Crazy Mike!"

We stopped. Sophie jumped out of the car and embraced Mike, introduced him to the rest of us, loaded his baggage in the trunk (the rope was used to scale the Pentagon wall) and we drove him to New York. On the way Mike told us that the Movement had escalated from protest to militant resistance, that nothing was unthinkable, that the Pentagon March was historically America's 26th of July (Castro's attack on the Moncada quarter in Santiago de Cuba) the defeat giving the Revolution ultimate victory. Despite my distrust of Castroite language, I hoped that Mike was right.

78

THE PORT AUTHORITY BUS TERMINAL IS A DEPRESS-ingly ugly building. It squats near Times Square on Eighth Avenue, windowless, rounded, hiding its rib cage behind its brick shell, bare to Ninth Avenue, clean to the bone. It is uglier inside than out. On November 23, 1967, less than a month after the March on the Pentagon, I stood four flights up on the cement skirt to one of the bus ramps, an over-creamed, bitter cup of coffee in my hand, my head swimming, looking rather bleary-eyed at the homely face of Roger. Roger is not the sight one likes to see at dawn after a hard night, sleepless, for Roger has, at twenty-one, the face of a tired failure, a revolutionary no one, not even his Detroit mother, takes seriously. That face! Hanging jowls, the muscles already weakened, the cheeks collapsing toward the nose, the entire face caving in on itself. Early. To say Roger looked like a bloodhound is to be kind. A paper bag Roger should wear over his head, especially at six in the morning when he is to join you on a bus trip to Princeton to attend a Regional Meeting of SDS where one's mind has to screw itself up to the task of revolutionary plotting, where one must adopt the proper revolutionary stance, trying to be neither too Leftist nor too Rightist as the center shifts continually.

"You look drunk," Roger said, looking charitably at my

red eyes, my shaking hands. "You shouldn't drink so much, not when you have to appear at a conference." Defensively I tried out my look of startled innocence, eyebrows raised, mouth dropped in astonishment. "Me? Drunk? Roger, I've never been drunk in my life!" I said, sounding drunk. He mumbled something about bourgeois decadence as we climbed aboard the bus.

Like good radicals we sat in the back. Roger sat next to the window. I on the aisle, my legs stretched out long under the seat in front of me. I closed my eyes and tried to think back on the party, wondering what the hell I was doing on a bus to Princeton with Roger peeling his everpresent orange next to me. I could *smell* the paper bag he always carried, peanut butter sandwiches inside, three oranges, the bottom of the bag stained wet with jelly droppings. For *this* I left Herbie's loft on Christopher, the light works pounding across my mind, the rumbling music, for this I should give up good liquor and the promise of sex—a vastly busted, vinyl-covered German Jewess, white leather boots, sparkling steel heels set to mark my back and thighs—and lights fondling the mind? Revolutions are not worth it, not at six in the morning.

I had gone to Herbie's pad at nine o'clock the night before to see a light show. I sat down on the couch, received a drink from the houseboy—who possesses the World's Most Enormous Cock and who lets you touch it if you allow Herbie to touch yours, a fair bargain, all things considered—and smiling at the nodding girl to my left, and smiling at the two boys cuddling on my right, and waving at Nat, an actor who looks like a butch Bette Davis, with short hair, the hysterical gestures, the overstatement, the staccato voice, I turned my attention to watching the show. Lights everywhere. Moving, whirling curtains of light that passed back and forth on the ceiling rollers, multicolored, blasting the mind. Four screens, each caught in its own craze, moving against my mind working with hash and scotch to blow it. Fading, I thought of

William Burroughs' image of one floating naked in absolute darkness in a pool of water maintained precisely at 98.6°, and in a few minutes one loses the capacity to distinguish where one's body ends and the water begins, where the demarcation lies between one and other bodies and the water; to float out of one's skin expanding consciousness, to become the water, to pass seemingly in and out of other bodies, to lose oneself utterly, to give way.

By one o'clock I was beautifully high, the girl was out of her mind on speed, Nat was jacking off watching the center screen, black and white, the room dark of everything but the pornography played in front of us . . . A *Nun's Story* . . . *Three Virgins and a Horseman* . . . *Stud Poker*. In she came, that huge German in vinyl, and stood, legs spread mannishly, her hands on her strong hips before a side screen staring out at the room. At five I left. Regretfully. The houseboy was standing on a chair in front of the screen, his pants dropped to his knees, waving the World's Most Enormous Cock with *both* hands, like a baseball bat, at the psyched-out room.

I walked in the cold to Sixth Avenue and waited for a cab and I thought of the coming SDS conference and how deeply involved I had become in radical politics. A few weeks before I had stood for hours before the Hilton Hotel with Mike and Al and Philip and thrown bags of red paint at the cars carrying to the Hilton guests of the Foreign Policy Association's dinner. It was the first organized off-campus demonstration where Columbia SDS played a significant role. There was violence. But this time it was expected and welcomed and used as a political device. Street politics. Confrontation. We stopped traffic. Got into fights. Paid special attention to attacking the car carrying Columbia's President, Grayson Kirk, into the meeting. It was the first time violent civil disobedience was used as a legitimate political tactic, at least in my experience, in New York. The meeting in Princeton was to determine if it was successful. My personal bias was that it was self-defeating, that equal numbers were alienated or won over by violence. And it was an unusual position for me to be in because Al (returned from Washington with an intense hatred of White America) and Philip (grown militant, disaffected to the point of quitting his fraternity, growing a beard, his language roughed into long fits of profanity) had moved to the Left of me. They wanted violence, revolution. They had a hatred of the cops and the government and established, corporate institutions I could not match. It was simply this: their feelings were of continuing outrage. They fed upon the war casualty lists, the tales of racist oppression in Harlem, the daily charges of Columbia's corruption (it was during the preparations for the protest against the Foreign Policy Association that most of us first discovered the links between Kirk and the Defense Establishment). With me the opposition to the System was less visceral, perhaps because I had experienced it longer. Except when personally threatened by the police, directly, or made witness to some vulgar cruelty against my friends, I was incapable of the depth of passion, the blind hatred that now consumed Al and Philip. I do not know why they reacted in that short period of time as they did. In part, at least with Philip, it may have been the suddenness with which consciousness came. Overnight. The U.N., and then he woke to the corruption which he had never *seen* before. With Al perhaps it was the overwhelming sense of vulnerability to the White Establishment. He had many white friends and lovers and yet they were not like him, they were *white* and in a sense unable in a profound and subtle way to really understand or share his experience. He was exiled twice over. Washington broke something inside. He no longer trusted us (and when the Columbia rebellion came he acted out that distrust of the whites by segregating himself with the other blacks, making emblems of us).

"Want a sandwich?" Roger offered, holding a dripping, gooey blob of peanut butter and grape jelly oozing between the bread. My stomach turned. "No, Roger." Sadist. "Are you sure? I've got plenty." "Quite sure, Roger."

Roger was a junior at Columbia. I first met him the year he appeared before a special disciplinary committee, headed by the then *Dean* David Truman, to hear charges against SDS members who had participated in an indoor demonstration.

I sat with him for days on end in the Faculty Room in Low Library, surrounded by jade vases stolen from China, listening to endless points of procedure and points of order and personal privilege while an exasperated Dean Truman worried about the press outside and the alumni committee and the Trustees and about his academic future. These punks, these *un*degreed kids had placed *his* sweated career in jeopardy. They had made a fool out of him, not exactly a difficult thing to accomplish considering his constitutional inability ever to admit that he was in the wrong. Truman had made an initial mistake. He had announced to the *Columbia Spectator* that he considered the students guilty of a violation of the rules and that they should be punished. But to us it did not seem kosher to have on a committee to establish the guilt or innocence of students a man who prior to the hearings had already made up his mind. It seemed unfair. Truman and Kirk failed to understand or admit our objection. Truman stayed on the committee but we made it hell for him. He sweated and fumed. Roger and the others made dramatic appeals to "academic freedom" and "human rights." I sat and listened half asleep.

It was not much of an event. Roger was placed on warning (which meant that if he got into trouble again he could be suspended). I got a chance to call Truman a "fascist pig." And I learned, as the others did, that the administration was hopelessly inept and somehow vitally paralyzed by its fear of public opinion. Like hypocrites in general, Kirk and Truman did not like to show their hand in public. Under Kirk's administration Columbia's ranking fell, distinguished professors left the University, the fragmentation of the institution continued at an increased pace. Things were looking bad. Kirk had a habit, a highly irritating one, of commissioning reports on Student Life, and faculty morale, and housing, and community relations and then suppressing them. Kirk and Truman lacked what the radicals had in abundance: an honest sense of justice. Thus the passion for maintaining academic form, for keeping up the front. I asked Professors Dodson and Trilling and Robert Gorham Davis how such political hacks wormed their way into administrative control of a great university. No one could tell me. And I still do not know.

An hour later we were in Princeton. The day was cold, gray, a light drizzle soaking through my "waterproof" discount house foreign correspondent's mackintosh, belt, epaulets, the works. I left Roger at the bus stop and watched him and Ted Kaptchuk, chairman of Columbia SDS, walk across the street to campus, heads lowered, deep in conversation. Before I followed them to SDS headquarters I stopped in a drugstore and had two cups of coffee, a danish, a slug of Pepto Bismol. I picked up a bus schedule so I could leave Princeton as soon as my stomach had had enough. I was in no mood to listen to eighteen hours of revolutionary speeches, to read unreadable radical leaflets, to play at outrage. Robert Lowell was right when he said that the radicals have no handsome style, they could not write, they could not speak. Not interestingly. Anger destroyed balance, and style depended on balance. All they had was anger. And that was not enough.

In the rain I walked four blocks to the SDS offices in the basement of a building that houses the Princeton student paper and other undergraduate organizations. Saturday, the middle of November, the day of the Yale game. The University was at its Ivy best. Self-conscious, trying bravely to live up to the myth of social eminence and power this side of paradise—THE LEADERS OF TOMORROW ON THE

84

PLAYING FIELDS OF PRINCETON—which Fitzgerald saw and caught at its end before the Great War and graced with a charm that passed with him. Its life was gone, stuffy, unspontaneous, funless; it had no importance now except to some freshmen and their parents and some frat boys and alumni, keepers of the myth, who needed badly to believe that it was real and counted for something in the world. As I walked under the wet trees, the grass thick and spongy, the air painfully clean in comparison to the filth I breathed in Manhattan, it impressed me that what was of importance at Princeton that day, what alone had the chance of touching history and of being relevant to American life, was the assemblage of scruffy, arrogant, intolerant, tasteless non-notables, non-Social radicals who would scheme while the game was played. They seemed real to me. The rest—the ivied buildings, the quaint, pseudo-English quads looking like Disney sets, the lovely, unused lawns, the parents and jock enthusiasms, the tweedy undergraduates with their Seven Sisters dates—fantastical, too clean and ordered and subdued and tasteful, far too correct, absurdly anachronistic in the America I knew—like gaudy old uniforms and antebellum houses. Gilding. It signified nothing.

I walked inside the SDS office. A young brunette, with heavy tits, braless, sat sprawling on top a desk on a pile of papers before immense posters of Che and Mao. She reminded me of the lightworks left and the German Jewess (I imagined her arm upraised in vengeful lust, powerful) lost to me now. She looked suspiciously at me as I came in out of the rain. I smiled and opened my coat and displayed my SDS and FUCK LBJ buttons. Certified, she handed me papers listing the conference's schedule. I thanked her and grabbed one long look at her breasts and marched dutifully over to McCosh Hall.

Like most SDS functions the meeting had not started on time. Most of the delegates were sleeping off a bourgeois hangover collected at an SDS party in Wilcox Hall the night before. Hours of Chinese Communist propaganda films are enough to drive the most temperate radical to drink (you know the type: brown photos of the Long March; badly translated speeches of Chairman Mao in Peking, his arms moving woodenly; scenes of millions in vast stadiums doing clockwork calisthenics; peasants with happy faces working knee-deep in rice paddies; charts proving China was leaping ahead of the United States in everything from babies to foot powder). Noting the misery, I felt good about my own drunk and went around consoling the few people in the room with Prohibitionist adages about that fatal glass of beer. A first class smart-ass, but I thought that for once I had a right to be. The puritans had it coming. I felt smug seeing them hungover by the most middle-class/middle-aged of vices. Hungover by something other than their bloody dreams and nights of plotting.

I was sometimes uncomfortable with the New Left, not because I disagreed in substance with its aims, but because I was often offended by its prejudice—the neo-Calvinism and anti-intellectualism it acquired from the drug scene, the superstitious distrust of success, and the envy, touched with Populism, that ran deeply in the American grain.

The New Left was decidedly American in character. It sustained a nostalgia for a simpler, better, quasi-rural age where men are strong and true and life is as uncomplicated as it is sweet (the hippies' impatience with and contempt for the technetronic culture had led them to create rural communes where they grew their own food, manufactured their own tools and comforts, and devised their own rules). "Participatory democracy" came from the legend of the Town Meeting and the Congregationalist traditions. The radicals' affectations of dress (the blue denim work clothes, the denial of personal luxury) and habit (poor living conditions, contempt for money and what it will buy) came out of the

American myth of the Common Man in homespun clothes, graced alone by his honesty and his hard freedom. Their sexual competitivelessness, their reluctance to admit to sexual distinctions, corresponded consistently with a refusal to make more subtle discriminations in matters of taste and style. A generation removed from the Depression, they romanticized poverty as being purer, more human than wealth. They made the life of the poor into a kind of theatre, a role-playing without actuality. Everything became symbolic. Most of them had never known hunger or the anxiety of poverty. They were the new aristocrats, young men jobless by choice.

Despite my dislike of their prejudice (I thought it produced a style that was often in large measure forced and conformist) I believed that for many young men with a highly developed moral sensibility a style such as the radicals affected was necessary to ethical survival in America. One had to avoid the market, the selling out. One had to consciously make oneself unattractive to the buyers if integrity were to be salvaged.

At Princeton I still wanted to be able to *believe* in American political and social structures, in their willingness and capacity to repair the national life. But I could not. I no longer believed in the essential decency of the American people, that given the truth the majority had the honesty and the compassion and the guts to do what was right and necessary. After the war was escalated again and again, and after police attacks on war resisters, after Arthur fled to Toronto and Rachel died and others were sent to jail and Philip and Al and the others were beaten and the SSS draft took more and more students to feed the death machine, after nothing was done to massively free the poor from their anguish, and after the assassinations and the busts—after America time and time again revealed herself to be violent and corrupt and this corruption started to directly affect my life and the lives of my friends, then I was taken beyond belief. Slowly, ineluctably, my attitude toward my country changed radically. Coldly.

In McCosh Hall I signed up for the workshop on Regional Action: Evaluation of November 14 and Possible Future Actions. I saw Mike in the hall outside the auditorium running the propaganda table. I bought a copy of Ogilvy's *Commitment and Change* (an excellent study of American economic imperialism by one of the founders of SDS) and then invited Mike to come with me for coffee. He told a girl to take his place at the table and off we went in search of a cafeteria.

As we walked I mentioned to Mike his remarks to me during the ride back to New York from Washington, his high praise of the Cuban Revolution and the New Order in China. He had said that the American liberal press vilified both revolutions and that the American people had never heard the truth about what went on in the Socialist camp. I countered by saying that I was opposed to all totalitarianism, whether Right or Left, and I did not think that one could, as Camus said, justify the death of present man in the name of future man. Here I was mouthing the left-liberal, social democratic, anti-Communism taught me at Columbia by Trilling and others who had developed their political stance against Communism during the Stalinist terror and the long years of the Cold War. It was then from Mike that I learned, really for the first time, how disreputable left-liberalism had become to the radicals. Mike explained revolutionary doctrine to me, advised me to read the correct books—among them Ogilvy, Debray and Fanon—and to think without a class bias, something which I was never conscious of doing before. I liked Mike very much because he was nice to me, never quite taking my political objections seriously, and because he was one of the few people I knew who could respect a man with whom he disagreed politically. And I think he believed that despite my left-liberalism my heart was on the right (that is, Left) side.

Mike and I went into the cafeteria in the basement of an old, neo-Gothic building (vine-covered, thick brown stone walls, moss damp and lush under the slate eaves) by the gates of campus. The room was crowded with Princeton students, dressed in neat blazers, flannel pants, striped school ties—irritatingly cleancut, finished bit players who lent themselves simply and unawares to caricature by the Left—and their parents, tanned in November, coated with good health and status, subdued. Expensive people. The Company Men. As we came in—I in my buttons and wet authentic foreign correspondent's mackintosh, Mike with his long, sandy-colored hair pulled into a Jeffersonian tail in the back, held in place by a silver and turquoise barrette, brightly colored beads dangling from his neck, bracelets, torn pants and suede jacket —the people stopped eating one by one, the room grew silent. They looked up at us, startled, obviously put off by our appearance. I thought this was probably the way these bastards stare at a servant who enters a room abruptly at the socially inopportune moment, or a stranger who violates one of their arcane rules which define who belongs and who does not. Mike and I did not belong. I despised the cake-eaters in the room, at once, deeply, very personally; I felt great malice toward them. If there was anything in my experience which helped to condition my heart against the economic and social order in America it was spending a childhood as a poor boy among relatively rich classmates. Now it seems silly that I would have allowed people for whom I maintain fundamentally such small respect to wound me so deeply, yet it happened. And I can appreciate, having experienced it myself, what it means to be a college freshman at Columbia or elsewhere without the funds or the connections to enter into a balanced social life.

Mike reacted to the stares by declaring very loudly, "When

the Revolution comes, baby, these capitalist pigs will be lined against the fucking wall." He then goose-stepped to the food counter and took what he wanted, giving the old lady at the cash register a surly revolutionary stare by way of payment. I followed him and played the sucker, paying both our checks.

Mike had used the same tactic before, on the trip back to New York from Washington, when we stopped for coffee at a restaurant on the turnpike in Delaware. He took food and coffee and walked by without paying. I, to avoid a scene, paid his bill.

When I joined him at the table he bitched me out, quite properly, for being oversensitive to spontaneous expropriation. "Direct action, man, not theft. Theft is a capitalist concept . . . *property* is theft. *Expropriation!* Like what happened in Cuba." As we sat and talked, more delegates from the conference found their way into the room and the straight set, finally outnumbered, abandoned the cafeteria to us.

Mike wanted me to second any motion he might make at the meeting. "We've got to radicalize this bunch of dead asses. There's a pack of unreconstructed liberals from Columbia," he grinned at me, "present company excepted, who are going to fuck this up if we don't stop them."

I asked him what he planned on proposing. "I want SDS . . . we're *supposed* to be the most radical group involved in the Whitehall [anti-induction] protest . . . that shows you how goddamn moderate this conference is . . . I want SDS to turn the Whitehall situation into a revolutionary event." Whitehall Street, where the main induction center in New York is located, was targeted as the next area of anti-Vietnam-war protest by a loose coalition of radical organizations in the city. Part of the purpose of the Princeton conference, in addition to examining the previous demonstration against Rusk, was to decide on tactics at Whitehall. "Those streets down there are made for barricades. Man," he said, warming to his subject, his speech taking on a characteristically hysterical tone, "all it'll take is some grease and broken glass and a few hand bombs and the streets . . . baby, they're so fucking narrow! . . . will be unpassable. Those goddamn horses and those fascist cop pigs won't be able to clear their ass in the crowd." I looked skeptical. He *is* crazy, I thought. "Otherwise," he continued, catching my doubt, "the pigs will trap us down there and the fascist thugs from Brooklyn and the Bronx will pour out of the subways and out of Battery Park and those goddamn, asshole longshoremen'll come through and we'll have our collective ass in a sling, man. And there's no question about that."

"For Christ's sake, Mike, if you provoke the cops you'll get murdered. We ought to try and keep the thing as non-violent as possible," I said.

"Bullshit, little boy!" Mike said, angered by my caution, "I don't fall for this non-violent shit anymore. Not at all. Because, pal, it's only *us* who stay non-violent. Not the cop pigs, the pigs are *paid* to shit on us. Paid, you know, like they got a *monopoly* on violence in this motherfucking country."

"Michael," I said, in my come-now-let-us-reason-together voice, "I thought the whole point of this conference was to work out plans so the demonstration would be *non*-violent. You understand? Locking arms, getting arrested without resistance, petitioning. The point's to *avoid* another Oakland-type riot." That month there had been long and bloody demonstrations against the draft in Oakland, California, led by the Berkeley chapter of SDS. Nearly ten thousand demonstrators had participated over a series of days, hundreds were arrested, scores severely beaten by the police. Joan Baez was among those arrested. What made the demonstrations significant is that they produced an escalation in tactics on the part of the anti-war movement. Streets were barricaded, property damaged, traffic stopped and young draftees were physically prevented from appearing before their draft board. It was also during this period that the first attempts were made to physically stop military trains by demonstrators lying on the tracks. The Oakland events excited the anti-war youth in New York, and the Whitehall protests, in part, were to be New York's contribution to the new militancy of the Left.

Mike looked up at me, grinning wickedly. "Dotson, baby, you got that crap about the purpose of this conference from where? One of our newsletters?" He laughed. "Man, don't you know by now never to believe an SDS press release?"

I laughed. "Who's the enemy here? I mean who's the CIA planted to lure us revolutionaries into non-violence?"

"Well, Mark Rudd's a Romantic. Revisionist. Never done a damn thing and he thinks the pigs'll kiss ass if you tell them it's a peace march. And Kaptchuk. He's no good. God, all he wants to do is buy and run mimeograph machines. Thinks you can convince the fucking liberals! Well, baby, it's a *liberal* government and a *liberal* war and those are *liberals* in Congress who pass war appropriations and increase the draft. You have to radicalize the liberals, wake the bastards up. And only violence can do that."

I thought of the peace protests and civil rights marches—endless, futile until the cruel violence of Selma, the death of three young men in Mississippi, the murder of Kennedy. Mike was right. It took someone's blood. And yet . . . ?

We left the cafeteria and walked back to McCosh. The rain had stopped, students again appeared in numbers on the lawns, carrying books and note pads, forming in small, animated groups before the library, chatting about the afternoon's game and the weekend. Mike and I and the several other SDS members I saw looked out of place on the campus. Intruders.

Near McCosh we caught sight of Mark Rudd walking into the building, his shoulders hunched up, his head down, eyes staring ahead, intense, his hands thrust in his front pants pockets, his feet moving in that odd, wide kind of walk he affected (because, I think, he believed it looked proletarian—

this son of the New Jersey middle class, fawned over by his parents, protected, playing the worker among his friends). He was typically dressed—blue jeans, a tan car coat, leather buttons bouncing on the cloth, open to the wind. Thick, brown, laborer's boots. Dark-blond hair, long, mussed. His large gray eyes. His silence. And I thought, as I saw him enter McCosh, that there was something unbalanced in his radical singlemindedness, something self-serving and unkind. I did not trust him. He was the only radical student I then knew at Columbia who was remorseless. Rudd was spooky.

Mike and I followed Rudd inside and then went into the room where the workshop was about to begin.

BREAD OR REVOLUTION was scrawled on the blackboard of the crowded classroom where the workshop was in session. Perhaps two hundred students sat before the I.W.W. slogan popular early in this century. It was appropriate that it was there because we consciously adopted the attitudes and style of the early American radicals, the anarchists, and Communists and labor organizers. While we despised present-day Communists, there was something attractive about the early radicals of the Left, their anger, courage and resolve.

Mike and I sat near the back of the room. I lit a cigarette and he sat next to me hunched over, picking his nose and giggling as a student from Princeton tried unsuccessfully to bring the room to order by tapping professorially with a pencil against the lectern. He got angry and pounded louder and started yelling, "Quiet! Please!" Nobody shut up. We ignored him and kept rapping away as if it were some kind of grand reunion after a battle and the survivors were delighted to be together once more.

In a sense it was a reunion. While some of the students at the Princeton conference had participated in the Pentagon March, it had been at their own initiative. It was not until November 14 (the anti-Rusk demonstration) that they acted as an SDS cadre and it was then that most of them experienced their first violent encounter with the cops.

"Look at him," Mike said, leaning over and pointing at Rudd, who was standing against the wall by the window, "Ain't he an arrogant son of a bitch." Arrogant he was. A Leftwing adventurist. The year before, he had gone to Cuba with a group of Columbia students. He returned infected by the violence of power and there he stood, the Revolutionary-As-A-Young-Man, watching silently as the discussion began, smirking, aloof, tolerating the stupidity of his friends, his eyes heavy-lidded, half-closed, sainted already.

Twenty years old, a junior at Columbia, he came from Maplewood (a suburb of Newark).

Mark Rudd. The grandson of Polish immigrants. His father a poor boy who made it (the usual route—the Army during the Second World War, retiring a lieutenant colonel; working for the Defense Department under Eisenhower; later making his bundle in real estate). Mark was a second son (his brother was a lawyer in Newark), a good Boy Scout, a good ham radio operator, a good but inattentive student in high school (Columbia in Maplewood) with enough cash to afford the Ivy League.

What was the trauma that compelled Mark Rudd against the Establishment in America? It was as ordinary as the occasional pain (or is discomfort the right word?) of seeing the wretchedness of the Central Ward in Newark from the window of his grandmama's candy store. Mark Rudd became a rebel with ease.

Mike and I listened as the workshop argued over tactics. Since most of us wanted a revolution in America we tolerated a wide latitude in discussion of the means. It was really the only thing we could do, since we could not agree on what kind of revolution we wanted or for what ends. We concentrated on perfecting tactics. At Princeton we spent our time defining the enemy (the Liberal Establishment. What else?) and the

94

tactics needed for victory. The emphasis was on the means which produce a country fit for revolution, how one brings about a revolutionary situation. For many of us at Princeton the means had become the end.

While all of us were veterans of some street or campus demonstrations (a few were currently under indictment for their role in the anti-Rusk protest) and while we were united, although rather tenuously, by varying degrees of hatred of privilege and capitalist wars, we were divided by ideological and tactical disagreements. The main division in our ranks was between the Leftwing adventurists and the "professional" revolutionaries (usually Marxist or radical socialist) who thought the situation in America demanded a greater emphasis on organization. This group, represented by Teddy Kaptchuk at Columbia (chairman of SDS who was eventually ousted by Rudd in March), wanted to expand radical political organization of teachers, ghetto residents, social workers, students and high school kids (this is the camp Rachel would have belonged to if she had lived). While they were concerned about the radicalization of educational institutions, their primary interest was much broader than simply bringing confrontation politics to campus. They wanted revolution and they believed that it would take years of hard organizational and propaganda work to bring it about.

Kaptchuk, a gentle young man, was more interested in intellectual political work than in activism. While Columbia SDS was militant under his leadership (more despite his chairmanship than because of it) its basic concerns were intellectual. It was Kaptchuk who initiated the studies of Columbia's expansion, its government contracts and its affiliation with military institutions. Kaptchuk's problem was that the newer members, among them Rudd, wanted to trip out on confrontation politics and leave the documentation and organization for others to do. In other words, Kaptchuk and the "professionals" were more political—they were interested

95

in the actual capture of power—and more patient than the younger radicals. That is, the younger members were more interested in dramatic confrontation with authority, no matter how futile, than in the seizure of power.

The group Rudd was aligned with was termed "Leftwing adventurist." They were reluctant to submit to any discipline (and the inability of the leadership to maintain revolutionary discipline over the membership during actual confrontation was one reason for the relative ineffectiveness of SDS up to that point). They tended toward anarchism and nihilism and they had a liking for the grand, symbolic gesture.

An example of this metality was demonstrated by my friend Terry. He no longer believed (who did?) that democratic dissent would bring about an end to the war. One day he asked a senior member of the faculty what he could do which might be effective in bringing the war to a conclusion. The professor, I think in all seriousness, suggested to Terry, who was twenty years old at the time, that he and his school friends form sabotage squads and go about the countryside blowing up military installations and other properties used in support of the war. Now, to me it seemed like a silly, half-ass idea, just the type of idea a middle-aged left-liberal professor would come up with. But Terry, being the anarchist he was, thought it was a splendid notion. Although he never did get around to blowing anything up, he still did not appreciate the danger of the suggestion.

One of the students at the workshop who ranted against Leftwing adventurists, whom orthodox Marxists considered revisionist in the extreme, said, "Our weakness is in discipline. At the Hilton we were to act as a group, organized with our own monitors to direct traffic and get at the limousines coming to the hotel. It failed. We were to avoid the cops and we confronted them. We were to stop only certain cars and we stopped all traffic. We were fucked up by those who can't wait, those who want to fight now. What we have to fight here, today, are the Leftwing adventurists. They want to get the pig *now*, Rusk *now*, Johnson *now*. Out of about eighty in the [Columbia SDS] chapter, ten are Leftwing adventurists and they're leading us blindly into December 4th. It's their dream, their wet dream! Idealists! Dreamers! They lead us to disaster!"

Mike poked me. "What's he mean, only ten? Shit, more than half, at least half!"

The speaker, to Mike's chagrin, spoke heatedly against SDS having anything to do with the Whitehall protests. His objections were tactical. The streets around Whitehall were too narrow. They would permit the police to corner and attack demonstrators while at the same time allowing them greater freedom because the press and spectators could be confined to remote areas. Whitehall itself was a poor choice because its security was unbreakable.

That was too much for Mike. He stood up, interrupting the speaker, and shouted, "Sure, the damn streets are narrow! They're *very* narrow. But narrow streets demand a change in tactics, a new kind of politics. Throw grease in the streets. The pig'll ride down the street but, man, it'll be one hell of a ride . . . we'll be sitting ducks there, you know, a bunch of dumb fucks waiting for the bastard longshoremen to club us down. And they will. Once it starts they'll pour out of them subways. We'll burn . . ." Mike was excited now; he could taste revolution burning, his vision close, possible, revolution! the end of the corrupt American state, ". . . but we'll burn the streets first. We'll be hit, but we'll hit the cops first." Here someone yelled sarcastically, "Pull down Whitehall! Like the Bastille!" Several people laughed, but Mike took it seriously. "You can't pull it down. It's a fortress. Literally. But it's the best possible fortress because of what it stands for. It'll be bloody, but blood makes the liberals mad. And we've got to make them mad."

The moderator, grown bold, told Mike to sit down. It was

too early to debate tactics. First it should be determined what the point of tactics in the Whitehall situation is before argument is opened about their use. Mike sat down, grumbling.

A girl from Vassar spoke. She sat on the edge of a desk near Rudd, her onyx-black hair combed long, straight, the ends curled on her shoulders, shimmering blue-black in the window light. Lovely black eyes, incredibly white skin. "I would like to say what I think our role is, if I may," she said, glancing at Mike, who had resumed picking his nose. "The role of students in this stage of the revolutionary movement is to plant seeds, to create alternatives, to make people disassociate themselves from a government which makes war. Americans have been raised to believe that this America is the great, white, liberal democracy, the place, Heaven. We must make them understand how evil the government is in order to win them to resistance. The polarity must be between the government and the people, not between the people themselves. We're wrong to focus their frustration and hatred against Johnson and Humphrey, to personalize it. It must be directed against the System, against *government* itself, against the *idea* of government. People must be made to understand that the government and the people represent two different Americas. They must be taught to distrust all institutions. All tactics are symbolic now. Disruption is needed. That is the most forceful kind of demonstration. People must be made to think!"

Her point about the necessity of disruption won general agreement. Her position was supported by a young man from City College who, Mike informed me, was a "sell-out."

"We aren't making resistance, but disruption. Rebellion is premature. Tuesday [November 14] was an attempt to disrupt the ruling class as represented in the Foreign Policy Association. Nowhere should they be allowed to meet in peace. We should be there every goddamn time to tell them that men will not suffer in silence. Not rebellion. Disruption.

And there the important criteria is effectiveness." He went on to oppose the Whitehall protest because he did not think it would be effective.

Rudd said, "Bullshit! Arrests, disorder. That's *always* effective."

A student from Rutgers stood up and went into a kind of emotional eruption. I do not know if it was Rudd's remark which set him off, or the speaker before, but his moment had come. "I'm a nihilist! I'm proud of it, proud of it! I want to fuck this goddamn country! Destroy it! No hope, not in fifty years. Tactics? It's too late. You're dreamers. Nowhere have I read or heard a Leftist say *how* to win today. We can't. So *fuck* winning! Let's break what we can. Make as many answer as we can. Tear them apart. They're corrupt and still they can't lose. We lose. So fuck the bastards!" He was shouted down. Emotional as he was, embarrassing in his intensity, yet he articulated the sense of futility, of appalling defeat which I felt very deeply and which every political act I attempted confirmed. And it was confirmed, too, in the disaffection of my friends, Al, Rachel, Mike, Philip, Terry, Sean and even Rudd, in the sense of orphanhood, of displacement each of them knew in America. Not to belong. A feeling as ordinary and sentimental as that. A conviction of failure before a beginning, a gnawing sense of loss. While all men are conscious of alienation, what I think was different about us is that we attempted to fix blame. We were judgmental. We wanted the bastards to pay. Goddamn it, to put an end to the sanctimonious bullshit, the shifting of guilt, the disavowal of responsibility which seemed woven into the fabric of American political and social life. The goddamn, piss-elegant, high and mighty phonies, the Rusks and Johnsons and Nixons and Humphreys, the frauds who presumed to dictate to the country what was and was not right. Patience forever preached. The liberal rhetoric used endlessly to bend men to accommodation before injustice and death. It was time to bring the house down even if it meant that we all burn.

Listening to him shout "I'm a nihilist!" I thought of the Harlem riots in New York and of staying those nights near Columbia and of being personally afraid for my safety and, at the same time, hoping the blacks had the guts and the stamina to do our work for us, to come avenging below the 96th Street line, to come burning and destroying. All of us in that workshop *knew* we could not win in America. That the rules were established in such a manner as to prohibit the possibility of radical change. That never had an industrial nation as advanced as the United States (take heart, Senator Goldwater) suffered revolution. Triumph was beyond us. Incapable of power, our lives were diminished to gesture. Symbols, for Christ's sake! It was stupid, I thought, knowing all that, to talk about effectiveness as an adequate criteria. *Nothing* was effective. That is why we were in Princeton plotting away like a pack of halfwits. The only thing we could do, and it would be frankly self-serving, was to escalate disorder, to increase confrontations increasingly abrasive. To undermine the faith of the people in the ability of the government to govern, in the safety of their streets, in the probity of their rulers. Out of this sense of preordained defeat I could understand later how a student could stand up and call for the assassination of the President. In a perverse way it was eminently logical.

The meeting broke early for lunch. I wandered around the Princeton campus. I heard the band play for the Princeton-Yale game. I saw students with their dates move toward the stadium. Seeing those young Americans going about life as if no war were being fought and no people were in prison for opposing it, as if Harlem and Watts and the Mississippi Delta country did not exist, as if the world were just and men were happy and did not die senselessly—seeing them I felt renewed

100

admiration for my radical compatriots. Divisive. Purists. Politically intolerant. Idealists. But committed to making the world finally more just and equitable. Gazers after a Four-square City with wild gates of pearl where peace reigns. For us at that time the desired was more actual, in terms of its influence on what we did, than reality. In our minds it existed for us. Somewhere in each of us the idea stuck that the earth had at one time been a better place and that somehow through effort and sacrifice the City of God would be constructed on this unhappy planet. We were patently anti-materialists, and, in a sense, anti-moderns.

Billy Graham told me that we (the disaffected young) were fair game for his preaching because we hungered after God but we did not know his name nor recognize his face. I think Mr. Graham flattered himself. Although the idea was imprecise, it did approach explaining what we were after. We wanted what did not now exist but which we obstinately believed *had* to exist.

Although most of us were agnostic at best, this romantic picture we had of life *after* the revolution, which for some resembled a crazed vision from the Revelation, was (I hate to use the word) religious in character. And I think it was this religious feeling about the future of life which accounted for much of our naiveté, stupidity and violence. Our *love* inspired us to dream of presidents murdered, tyrants hanging by their heels in public parks in Washington, the land ours. Free at last, brother, free at last.

As I walked across campus to a coffee shop near the bus stop I thought of Al and what he had told me one night after we had sat up bitching about Columbia. It was during the period when the University's affiliation with the Institute for Defense Analysis and its connection with several CIA conduits were becoming public knowledge. Corruption all over the fucking place. The cake-eater Trustees and their toady administrators playing with the lives of our friends, supporting the war, these bastards who justified the University's refusal to condemn the war by bullshitting that the University was above politics, while at the same time they rendered a deadlier, more heinous support to the war. That night Al had said, talking about how antithetical to us (to our values) America seemed, Al said, "When's America going to come true? Man, when is she going to come true for *us?* How long we got to wait until she becomes *our* country, until she becomes *like* us? How long, baby, how goddamn long?"

What we knew (which the liberals generally refused to admit even after the McCarthy campaign and the Chicago disgrace) was that constitutional procedures were not functioning in America, that democracy was a failure, a farce, a series of meaningless forms which had very little to do with the transfer of real power. We knew that justice could not be won through democratic channels. Extraconstitutional instruments for the radical restructuring of American institutions had to be devised. But we were so *outside* the System, so completely removed from the operation of power, that we no longer bothered to consider traditional "democratic" political mechanisms as viable. New and radical forms had to be created and invested with power. We were convinced that these new forms, when they emerged, would involve confrontation, disruption and violence. And they would be welcomed.

My left-liberalism was so moribund that afternoon that when a girl suggested the assassination of President Johnson I did not accept my own opposition to the idea. (One of the odd phenomena of the young, radical Left is the militancy of the females. By far the girls, in a confrontation situation, are the most prone to violence. They tend to nag the boys on.) For most of us assassination, as a political technique in the United States, was patently unthinkable. It had always been unthinkable to me. But when she stood in the meeting and suggested the novel idea of considering the *theoretical* possibility of killing "that pig in the White House" my response was ambivalent and weak. I did not believe the words I was saying in opposition to her suggestion.

The greater part of the afternoon session was spent in defining the Enemy—the Liberal Establishment—and attempting to reach agreement on the ultimate ends of resistance.

One of the girls from Columbia (Rebecca was her name. She was blond. Beautiful, in a tough, sexy sort of way. Tall. And she dressed with an awareness of style which was beyond the hope of most of the SDS women who were, let's admit it, friends, dogs) talked about the Enemy. "Elsewhere in the world people are oppressed, the majority is oppressed. Force is obvious everywhere in those countries. Here it's disguised. Here the liberal's the enemy. They lead a silent majority turned on by the idea of democracy, the public forms. And that majority's been bought. The *liberal's* got to be exposed. It's a liberal war in Vietnam. They're the warmongers, the power brokers, the enemy. . . . We must polarize the government, the liberal's government, against the people. Americans are idealists. We have to make them see that the government offends that idealism."

Rebecca proposed to do this through a series of escalations of resistance. "Make each demonstration more violent until the government is forced to pass repressive laws and take general repressive actions which attack the innocent with the guilty. The government," she stated, "will collapse if Americans can be convinced that it can't maintain order except through strong-arm, fascist methods. The country's fascism has to be made public through its acts against its citizens."

Rebecca was correct in what she said. Most of us agreed with her. The regrettable thing was that we could not agree on the specifics of the government to replace the one she had just overthrown.

The next speaker supported Rebecca's thesis on the escalation of resistance. He told of how protesters at the anti-Rusk demonstration rushed against police lines and then fell back into the mass of the crowd lining Sixth Avenue. The police, in response, charged into the spectators and, unable to distinguish the demonstrators from innocent bystanders, tore into everybody. "Women, some in evening dresses, who stood there hating us for being dirty and loud went home hating the pigs and the man [Rusk] they were protecting. Via disruption we have to implicate the indifferent, the innocent, so to speak. Plan strategic interruptions which will force the government to increase its control over the civilian population until they'll tolerate government no more. Like at Washington. The 'Negotiate Now' people got hit over the head and some of them got the blindness knocked out of them by the pigs. Those people . . . you have to take it home to those people. The fat liberals. They only act when they're hurt."

A boy from Boston said, "We have to make it politically expedient for one of the national parties to nominate a candidate who'll end the war."

Rebecca interrupted him, shouting over him impatiently, "What the hell is this? I do not see ending the war as our goal. Not really. Whoever's elected won't stop the war. And even if they do, so what? The killing'll go on, if not in Vietnam then somewhere else. God, let's admit it! Elections, parties, they're not worth a damn. They can't bring change. Ever. Make it bloodier until the Americans can't take it anymore, until they have only one alternative—to overthrow the liberal, capitalist system that makes war necessary."

"The end, brothers and sisters," Mike said next, finally letting out the darkness, "is revolution. Opposition to the war is a pretext to create a revolutionary situation. Check off the fucking liberal middle class. Check off the fascist unions. We only need three percent of the population to make a revolution!"

The afternoon passed. People began to leave. The rain began again. The mood grew heavy. Conversation turned to disruption at our own universities. Columbia, Boston University, New York University, City College and Yale were considered most vulnerable to attack. Taking hostages, student strikes and the blocking of buildings were offered as possible tactics for exerting pressure on the educational managers. But in the quiet depression of that late afternoon at Princeton none of us really had much hope for campus rebellion that year.

Before we left the conference it was agreed to let each individual decide whether he would protest at Whitehall or not. We did not think the induction center would be shut down.

Before I took the Greyhound bus home I had coffee with Roger, Mike and Rebecca. We agreed to meet at Whitehall.

chapter seven

IF YOU HAVE EVER GONE THROUGH THE PRE-INDUC-
tion physical at Whitehall in downtown New York and you
come back later and see the building, just the memory of the
power of the military over your life (assuming you escaped)
demonstrated at Whitehall scares the *hell* out of you.

During the first week of December I sat for three hours
waiting for Rebecca to meet me at the West End Bar. She
came in about ten o'clock. It was a very cold morning and she
was wearing a red cloth coat with a fur collar, high vinyl boots,
and a red scarf. She looked very pretty, her hair blond and
framing her face flushed by the wind. We had coffee and some
eggs and then took the subway downtown. By the time we got
near Whitehall the police had blocked off the access streets.
We could not approach the induction center.

We spent several hours marching around in a crowd of
anti-war protesters whom the cops skillfully kept moving in
circles around the Whitehall blocks. It was cold. It was irritating.

About one o'clock Rebecca and I heard that there were to be
demonstrations against the draft in Battery Park. We walked
over to the park, stopping once to buy some roasted chestnuts
from a vender. At the park the police had cordoned off the

main area and behind their security lines perhaps fifty demonstrators, most of them college students, faced a mob of perhaps one hundred longshoremen. Burly, mean bastards. America First types. The kind who never buy Polish hams. The police allowed the longshoremen to slip through into the sealed area but no more anti-war demonstrators were allowed to enter.

Rebecca and I stood together watching the anti-war people walk around in a circle, carrying signs reading, "End The War!" "U.S. Get Out Of Vietnam!" "Stop American Imperialist Wars!" They were brave, those radicals, trooping around in the cold, shouting slogans while the unionists watched, growing angry. Standing with Rebecca I wanted very badly to join the demonstrators in the circle. I wanted to join them because they were cold (some did not even have on winter coats. Young radicals never seem to dress warmly enough. No gloves. No coats) and, even though there were many cops present, they were in possible danger. Also we had arrived too late to get to Whitehall itself and I felt disappointed, robbed of effect. While they marched, Rebecca and I and about a score of sympathetic spectators shouted encouragement. The longshoremen milled in a pack about twenty yards from the anti-war group. Except for an occasional demand that the demonstrators go back to Russia where they came from, the longshoremen were silent.

One of the longshoremen walked up to one of the demonstrators and he pulled the demonstrator's sign from his hands and hit him in the face with it. A fight broke out. The longshoremen attacked the demonstrators, beating them with their fists, kicking them, tearing apart their signs; brutal, unprovoked, done while the cops prevented us from joining our friends and our friends from joining us.

Rebecca and I shouted MOTHERFUCKING FASCIST BASTARDS at the longshoremen and the pigs. It was beyond belief. Rebecca hit the cop in front of her with her hand. He turned around. "Do something, goddamn it!" she shouted at him. "Stop it! Stop it!"

The cop, a rookie patrolman with a handsome, open Irish face (there are times when strangers are at a moment so important that their face is remembered. His face I remember as I remember the face of one of the troopers at the Pentagon. Both were young and vital. Both were incongruous with their uniforms) turned around and looked at Rebecca, a faint smile on his face. "Quiet, lady. No disturbing the peace. Against the law." He said it straight, without a touch of irony.

Rebecca was stunned. The longshoremen's assault against the demonstrators lasted about ten minutes and then the cops moved in and broke it up, arresting the demonstrators.

I stood watching, dumbstruck, shivering, unable to recognize what I was witnessing. Fun City.

We took the subway uptown to Columbia. Already the Christmas placards were up above the windows of the train. The car was crowded. Rebecca found a seat and I stood before her, holding on to the metal ceiling strap with both hands, my head bowed between my arms, looking down at her. She said nothing. She sat staring ahead at my waist. She thought me a coward. I had lost. I knew it and it angered me. And standing swaying with the motion of the train, a half an hour after the beatings in the park, a half an hour after I was once more made aware of both my vulnerability to violence and my impotency before it (and unlike many other things, violence never ceases to excite, it never becomes banal except at a great distance), thinking of the kids getting beaten and of our shouting at the longshoremen and of the cops' refusal to enforce the law (the law! shit!) and thinking of Rebecca and my inability to protect her, standing there I got an erection as the train moved uptown, overheated, rumbling, dirty, and I stood hard-on, thoroughly unself-conscious, unembarrassed, indifferent to it, partially hoping that through the cloth she might notice, and partially not giving a goddamn if she didn't, in my mind I accepted without question the symbiosis of manhood (sex) and violence. Defeat.

chapter eight

On February 28, about two hundred of us marched to Low Library to protest the presence of recruiters from Dow Chemical (the napalm makers) on campus. The picketing of the administration building was led by Ted Kaptchuk. Several of the militants demanded that we leave Low and go over to Dodge Hall where the Dow recruiters were. Kaptchuk opposed the idea. He did not want trouble. His opposition did not mean a damn because we ignored him and went over to Dodge Hall anyway and sat-in. It was not much of an event. I went home soon after it began because nobody was paying any attention to us, except the Dow men who ran away, and it seemed silly to sit on a floor and have people walk around you as if you were not even there. It was mortifying. We sat-in. That was all there was to it. That, and the fact that Kaptchuk and the moderates lost effective control over what SDS might be able to do.

The next day we marched over to the gym site in Morningside Park where the University was trying to build a new college athletic facility. There were a lot of cops there. We tried to pull down the link fence surrounding the site. The cops stopped us. Brian got hit in the stomach by a sergeant. About a dozen students were arrested. Rudd made a dumb speech. I thought the whole thing was stupid. It was stupid to think you could stop Columbia from stealing park lands and playing White Massa to Harlem by pulling down a fence. It didn't make any sense.

About a month later a hundred SDS members invaded Low Library and held a short demonstration against the Institute for Defense Analysis. Kirk got pissed about the noise and he invoked his new rules against indoor demonstrations. Rudd was now chairman of SDS (poor Teddy Kaptchuk was bounced. Nobody likes a moderate) and he and five other students were put on probation by the University. It did not seem fair, their being placed on probation, since we had been making demonstrations on campus, in and out of buildings, for years and no one had been disciplined for it before. And now Kirk decided, after the fact, that it was wrong and against the rules and intolerable and naughty and patently UnAmerican. But Kirk was an ass.

By April the campus was divided over the gym issue, over the punishment of the six students, over the University's affiliation with the Institute for Defense Analysis and other Defense Department institutions. Most of the students and faculty were fed up with Kirk and Truman and the Low Library boys and the Trustees and the refusal of the administration ever to consult any member of the University community about decisions which affected their lives. The administration remained arrogant and removed and incredibly insensitive. Scared.

Tuesday afternoon, April 23, approximately a hundred radical students, led by Mark Rudd, marched again to Morningside Park. Again an attempt was made to pull down the fence surrounding the construction site. Again the police were called. Rudd led the students away, leaving the cops and the administration with the impression that the day's protest was over. Instead of dispersing, Rudd directed the SDS demon-

111

strators in an attack upon Hamilton Hall (originally Low Library was to be invaded but the administration had wised up and the building was sealed), a classroom and administration building of Columbia College. The Acting Dean of the College, Henry S. Coleman, was in his office and the building was closed by SDS. Contrary to the press reports, Dean Coleman was not held hostage (who the hell would want to ransom him?). He simply would not leave. Wanted to protect the furniture.

The building was secured by four o'clock. About four-thirty, Tom Hayden arrived in Hamilton Hall as planned. It was Hayden's decision that produced the withdrawal of white students from Hamilton, leaving the building in the sole possession of the blacks. Al was among the black brothers who segregated themselves in Hamilton. Some members of the SDS Steering Committee opposed Hayden's decision, yet tactically it was an astute move, for it effectively prevented the University from acting against the seizure of Hamilton Hall. (Rap Brown, on the following day, was the first in a chorus of black radicals who would inform the University that if the police moved against the black students, the University would be burned to the ground.)

Later that day, after they had been kicked out of Hamilton by the blacks, about two hundred white SDS members went charging over to Low Library. They broke into the building and took over the President's Office. With Low occupied the administration attempted to split the radicals by negotiating separately with Hamilton Hall. The blacks would not be bought.

On Wednesday night students from the School of Architecture, not connected with SDS, took over Avery Hall. The occupation of the buildings began to get wider student support.

Shortly after midnight on Thursday the police were called to campus. Vice President Truman informed the faculty (meeting ad hoc in Philosophy Hall) that the police had been asked to restore order on campus. His announcement was greeted by shouts of "Shame! Shame!" and "Resign!"

That night, two days after the Liberation began, I stood in front of the doors of Low Library trying to prevent the police from entering. Inside the President's Office the students were busily photostating the President's private files. Those of us standing before the doors of Low considered it unthinkable that the administration would order the cops on campus. It was, as one faculty member put it, "A violation of trust. A betrayal. Kirk breaks the damn rules if he calls in the cops."

The cops came. In plainclothes. They moved through the crowd of faculty and students and at one point their passage was blocked and they used the nightsticks hidden under their coats to force passage. One instructor was hospitalized with a head injury. Several other faculty were hurt. We were goddamn angry.

While we were trying to act bravely in front of Low, other students were calmly seizing another building.

Tom Hayden led a group of thirty students to the front doors of Mathematics, a large building that sits on the Broadway perimeter of the Columbia campus diagonally across from Low. When they arrived they were met, as prearranged, by a member of the Math teaching staff who had a key to the building. The doors were opened.

Once they had entered Mathematics the next problem was to get into the library, which occupied the southern half of the main floor, in order to get chairs and tables to use in building barricades. The library was locked and the two cleaning ladies inside refused to open the doors. One of the students smashed the glass on the door. The student rebels poured into the library, taking the furniture the women had been dusting minutes before and throwing it against the main doors and tunnels. The cleaning women were informed that

113

their building had been liberated. They were allowed to leave through a window.

Willie, who was a freshman from Canada, went searching for keys to the rooms. In the kitchen he found a set and opened about two-thirds of the building. Most of the offices remained locked.

Late that night, near dawn, I climbed through the access window into Mathematics and joined the Liberation.

chapter nine

FUCK GRAYSON KIRK WAS SCRAWLED ABOVE THE URI-
nal in the downstairs men's room of Mathematics, a building
occupied by two hundred SDS-led students, former hippies,
former left-liberals, the formerly apolitical, uninvolved, apa-
thetic, safe. I studied the graffito, trying to take my mind off
the fact that I was urinating in a liberated bathroom four feet
from where two Barnard freshmen were washing up. They
were on the Food Committee, breakfast corps. It was six
o'clock Sunday morning. I needed a bath and a shave and a
Bloody Mary, in that order.

I stood, it seemed for hours, cock in hand, erect, leaning
tightly against the cold wall of the urinal, wishing the girls
would leave. Nearly a week, and I had not learned the revolutionary art of sharing bathrooms with women. I stood
planted to the tile, ignoring the girls' giggling, staring dumbly
at the wall. What if they *never* leave, I thought, I'll be stuck
here like the madman in *Marat/Sade*, hard cock permanently
erect, while they wash and wash and wash.

Sunday morning. I was hung over. The night before I had
attended a long meeting in the main lounge, chaired by Tom
Hayden, where we had argued about negotiations with the
administration and the faculty. Around midnight I had gone
up to the fourth floor and found Brian and Terry and Willie

115

—he wearing a white cardigan the police later left stained with his blood—sitting inside a faculty office, the lights off, drinking the scotch and beer they had brought into the Mathematics commune before it went dry. Saturday night. We climbed into the attic of Math. We opened the window in the roof—you could see the stars that night, the air was cool and smelled of fish and of the sea—and Terry, his green eyes catching the light, sat under the bare bulb, with the three of us seated around him drinking, and quoted poetry by heart—his own, Ginsberg's and Dylan Thomas'.

Six hours later, Sunday morning, the bathroom and the giggling freshmen. FUCK GRAYSON KIRK.

I went into the main floor lounge in search of coffee. My headache was growing. It rumbled through the room making me literally lust after a shot of Pepto Bismol. I hurt. Most of the students were still sleeping, but a few were beginning to get up, taking their blankets off the floor, moving toward the bathrooms, waking up. I leaned against the counter, found the coffee, heated the water, looked over the room. Before we took Math the lounge had been part of the library. Now the furniture was serving as barricades before the front doors and tunnels, the library shelving was nailed against the windows, and the place—for one brief week—was being used humanly by the young.

I took the coffee and climbed two flights of stairs, maneuvering over fire hoses uncoiled down the steps, squeezing past piles of chairs waiting to be sent tumbling down when the first cop came, past little cardboard trays of vaseline and mounds of plastic bags to be used against police gas.

In the dining room lounge. In a thick, soft chair. Asleep.

"You're not drunk *again?*" Roger said, hitting me over the head with *The New York Times*. "You've got a real problem there with booze, Dotson. About every time I see you, you're hung over." Compassionless exaggeration. The prude.

I smiled at Roger. Why, Dear God, why every morning

when I need a little sleep after a little drunk, why is it Roger's homely face I meet? "Roger," I said, "I had a drink with some comrades in the attic last night. Celebrating the Liberation. Good, clean fun, Roger. A drunk, but a *political* drunk."

He passed me a look of moral disgust and plopped into the chair beside me and opened, you might know, *another* paper bag stinking with peanut butter and jelly sandwiches. He looked knowingly at me and then glanced proudly down at his lunch bag and then looked to me again, offering me with his eyes one of his homemade, juicy, protein-packed peanut butter sandwiches. No thank you, Roger. And then, *knowing* the condition of my stomach, he reached fiendishly into his paper sack and pulled out deviled eggs wrapped in wax paper and began munching away. The eggs were not so bad, but it was the smell of the eggs *plus* the ketchup on the eggs *plus* the peanut butter *and* the jelly *and* the oranges which started the flutters. Christ, I thought, for *this* we took five buildings and disrupted a university, for *this* we faced jail, so Roger could carry a paper sack, like a badge of martyrdom, around with him and inform anyone who asked how he *knew* from *much past experience* that jail food was uneatable? Better to be prepared at all times, he advised. Carry peanut butter sandwiches in paper bags. Be ready when the fascist bust comes.

I closed my eyes again. I woke to the sound of WKCR, the campus station, blaring out over the room. Roger had left, leaving only curled orange skins to mark his passing.

Students were relaxing in the room, some reading *The New York Times* and laughing, some playing cards, a few gathered around a card table painting posters: GYM CROW MUST GO! Over WKCR pompous professors were bitching about the fact that the majority of Columbia students opposed the Liberation (doubtful) and that the "overwhelming number" of students in the occupied buildings were being "duped" by SDS. So what? It mattered for nothing since this was the first event in most of our lives where we felt effective, where what we were doing belonged to us. Never before had I felt as effective as during the Liberation. I had been in the Peace and Civil Rights Movements. I had worked through countless protests, picking up friends at each: Mike at the Pentagon, Roger at Princeton, Philip at the U.N., Rebecca at Whitehall —where we stood outraged, held back by the police, and watched our friends beaten up in Battery Park by ignorant, half-ass longshoremen.

I sat there and wondered where Lionel Trilling was, hoping that somehow he, who wanted to understand so badly what was happening to us, would come over to our side. I remember telling him that in relation to his generation we felt disregarded, unconsulted, powerless—powerless to affect the quality of our lives in his America. Our lives, without roots in history, seemed diminished to gesture, without power to desperation, without probable hope to fantasy. With that fantasy our politics and art were being created, a fantasy of revolution and ritual murder and the giving way to a clean violence and a final peace. Even sitting in Math was a bit fantastic, unreal, hopeless, for I knew that they could bust us anytime they wanted. There will be no revolution, and good, rich, respected men will die, as always, in their beds.

But it did not matter. None of it. Not the bust to come, nor the degrees and careers in jeopardy, nor the liberal faculty insulted and lost. All that counted was the two hundred of us in solidarity for the first time together, together in our place in our time against the cops outside and the jocks outside. HIT THOSE RED PUNK FAGGOTS AND HIT 'EM HARD! It did not matter, for if you truly believe—and we were true believers—that your hope of change is all you have, even in as narrow a situation as Columbia, and if you suspect that it is false, that you can finally do nothing effective to act on its behalf, then you have to choose between throwing it over or keeping it and acting against your suspicion. We acted against our suspicion. Our outrage grew and, in time, fermented into hatred. In five days inside the commune at Columbia I learned again to hate with a passion things I had once loved.

But I could not see any alternative to being in the building with my friends, to acting in every situation in rebellion against the System. What other choices were there? Trilling's generation had covered all the options. We were left with our resistance and, in this culture, that meant acting in danger to ourselves. It always cost *us*. At the anti-Rusk demonstration I saw young men rush at mounted police in the hope of being clubbed. At the Pentagon we waited late into the night—Lowell and MacDonald had parties to attend—in the growing tension and the cold, waited around fires built on the steps before that massive, ugly building, waiting, hoping in the dark that the troopers' fingers would tighten and the bullets would fly and it would be over for us. We wanted to force them to act irrevocably. We wanted a response *to us*. Any kind. And now at Columbia I waited, knowing they could not act affirmatively in regard to us, they could give nothing without endangering the whole fucking System. I wanted them to act as they must, to act against us, to reveal themselves for what they are—a stinking, rotten group of men. "We have to consider," President Kirk had said, "what effect our actions will have on other American universities." I and the others had reached the point where we could no longer tolerate being disregarded. I and the others had to own our lives.

Terry came into the dining lounge and asked, "When do we eat?" I told him around noon as usual. He sat down beside me, took a notebook out of his pocket, and started writing. He looked up once to ask me if I knew a word that rhymed with Trotsky. I didn't.

Terry's father is a landlord. A conservative. Terry had walked out a year ago and gone to Haight-Ashbury and become active in the Oakland anti-draft riots. When he came back he said, a bit dramatically, "I saw the face of America out there. And it is made of violence." Terry is very bright and very gifted and yet he does not want to go back to school, he does not want to go to graduate school, and he will not go into business or government. He does not want money or power. He does not want to live off someone else's labor. He does not want to sell out. He said to me that he felt like someone lying on his back in a cellar with a low ceiling. And he can hear music and laughter filter down to him. And he presses his hands against the ceiling trying to find out where it is weak, where it will break and let him into life. Yet it will not break for him.

On Friday morning when we entered the liberated building I asked him if he knew he was liable for arrest. He nodded that he knew. "It is part of the game," he said. He wants a revolution in America. He does not know how to make one. So he hangs loose. "I am looking for the inside of a jail." He thinks it is pure there because he sees the outside as being corrupt and deadly. "A jail is in all our futures," he said. And he wrote, "I see my manhood in the streets." That was in Oakland in the riots.

Terry wrote. I read *The Times*. I was astonished at the inaccuracy of the reporting of the Columbia rebellion. Remembering that its publisher Sulzberger was on the Columbia Board of Trustees made it seem sinister. The radio was still blaring out reports of activities on campus; jocks had surrounded Low Library and they were mumbling about Taking The Situation Into Their Own Hands. Acting Dean Coleman (was he seeing perhaps a real, permanent, high-paying, high-status deanship in his future—the lure of it all shimmering just beyond those Trustee asses, bow and kiss?) was going around trying to keep the boys cool, telling them that "Harlem surrounds us. They'll burn the place down if we're not careful, fellows. Let's have the police handle the situation. You can trust President Kirk," etc. The boys were getting impatient. It is no fun to be called dummy jocks by long-haired, dirty—but oh so bitterly bright—radicals and not want to beat them up. Especially when they whispered that there was something peculiar about your masculinity in your posturing love of violence.

The jocks were grouped on the lawns before the buildings. The police sat muzzled in the basement of Low and other buildings waiting to be unleashed. And outside, along the walls of Math, more cops stood in the sun, looking up now to see the students throw Sunday flowers down on them from the lounge. Faggots with their flowers. Sick!

We had tuna fish and tomatoes for lunch. After eating I went on to the ledge overlooking Broadway and sat down beside Willie. He had his shirt off—handsome, well built—and I took mine off and we sat together in the sunshine passing Coke bottles and cigarettes from mouth to mouth. Beautiful. Down below people walked by, some of them stopping to put money or food in our bucket, others calling out obscenities, most, however, simply raising their fingers in a Churchillian V, our symbol of victory. As usual there were a dozen or so cops leaning against the wall, most of them quite young, some even well disposed to us. Privately.

A contingent of Harlem demonstrators marched by with signs protesting the construction of the gym (HANDS OFF HARLEM) and shouting, "Strike! Strike!" They were the poor. In the street the middle-class, Uncle Tom niggers swept by in their shiny new cars trying to look as disdainful as possible, Thoroughly East Side Token Nigger, more white than us, giving us sliding glances of contempt as they roared by; some, playing White Tourist, slowed their cars and rolled down the windows and pointed up at us with queenly "we-are-amused" type smiles just like the Man does when he goes slumming in Harlem on Sunday afternoon. It was sad, their self-hatred.

A blue Ford pulled up and double-parked in front of the building. A middle-aged man, stout, gray-haired, looking like

121

a Prussian shopkeeper or a Southern preacher, got out of the car, a Bible carried in his right hand. He came over and stood a few feet from the Math building, his hands on his hips, and looked up at us, trying to shrink us with his contempt. He yelled up at us: "If My people which are called by My name shall humble themselves and pray and seek My Face I will heal their land...." Willie, seeing his Bible, hearing God shouted in the street, interrupted him, "Thou shalt steal, Columbia!" The man began again, louder: "If My people which are called by My Name...." "Thou shalt not kill, America!" The man stopped. He gave Willie the finger. "Fuck you Commie bastards," he shouted, "God fuck you bastards!" And then seeing the girls lining the ledge with us, twenty feet above him, out of reach, casually dressed flower children, lovely in the sun, seeing them smile down on him, he started to shout hysterically: "Bitches! Whores of Babylon! Where would you be if some big, black buck was raping you in an alley? Red sluts! Who'd you call, you Commie cunts! Who'd you call for help? The *police*, that's who you'd call, you Communist...." While he was spewing forth into the street a rookie cop calmly walked over to his double-parked Ford and gave him a parking ticket. We applauded. The cop grinned and bowed in reply.

Willie slapped my thigh and laughed. "Beautiful, baby. The world's beautiful! You, the cops, life... life's so goddamn beautiful!" I smiled back at him. He put his hand to my head and playfully mussed my hair.

Sitting on the ledge that Sunday afternoon, caught by his friendship, I felt a great sense of oneness with the people of the commune. We were together until it was ended for us. Our building—*our* home, for Christ's sake!—where we slept and ate and talked and bathed and worked together. And our sensitivity to the goodness of the commune experience was born out of a consciousness of its contingency—that in point of fact it was bounded by time and place, fatally weak, impossible of survival. We had to make it last as long as we could. We had to make it good. Our tolerance of each other was immense. In the week, I heard not one word said in anger against anyone in the commune. And sitting with Willie on the ledge, full of love for him, I thought of Camus' celebration of human solidarity in *The Plague* and of Alyosha in *The Brothers Karamazov* with the children at the funeral, telling them to remember their sometime oneness with each other. It was a tender sentiment, in its constancy of strength new to me, and it was decidedly unusual in my America. It was, at the risk of sounding hopelessly sentimental, a precious thing.

Around five the general meeting of the commune began in the main lounge. There was one held each night. Participatory democracy. Hayden chaired them. Terry and Willie and I sat on a rug in the back of the room, not paying much attention until an announcement was made by the Steering Committee that it had broken off negotiations with the Ad Hoc Faculty Group. This frightened me since I assumed that the administration would not chance mass resignations by calling a police bust while the faculty was negotiating with the students to end the occupation of the buildings. That, of course, was precisely what happened, there being no honor among liberals or thieves. Not with so much at stake, so much *loot* to peddle one's liberal ass for—research grants, government appointments, secret funds, POWER. Not even the faculty is worth losing Percy Uris' millions. Not to mention the Rockefellers'. *Gawd!*

There was a brief debate over the accuracy of the announcement; two students, one of them was Philip, disagreed about what exactly had happened at the Steering Committee meeting they had both attended. I was getting nervous so, true to left-lib form, I took the floor and made a brief and, as I remember it, magnificent speech in defense of Trilling and Westin and Anderson, the professors from the Ad Hoc

Faculty who had just come under attack. I remember calling them "eminent, fair-minded," and saying the students could act in "complete good faith" with them. The radical leaders particularly disliked the "eminent men" line, thinking, probably correctly, that it sprang from a nasty little case of intellectual elitism—most undemocratic—that I was coughing up into the room. To protect the commune from my counterrevolutionary remarks they proceeded to attack the faculty all over again, this time making it most personal. Undeterred by the evidence, I made another neat speech and offered a motion directing the Steering Committee to do what it was most unwilling to do—reopen negotiations with the faculty. I was not the only closet elitist in the room, for my motion passed overwhelmingly.

It *is* hard overnight to see your professors as enemies tainted by bloody CIA funds. It is hard but, more often than not, it is true. The University was corrupt. And much of the faculty was complicit in its corruption.

Flushed with the victory of my motion I stood, not really knowing what to say, to propose other motions. *Many* of them. I did not want to let my moment of power pass. I had the Majority! I was a Leader! Not like the others who had only one gripe to bitch, I discovered as I stood to the floor, Hayden looking impatiently in my direction, that I had hundreds of silly motions whirling in my head, motions about the use of the bathrooms, the lousy food, the Defense Committee and, *most importantly*, the ban on drinking. I could have stood the entire day offering motions to be rubberstamped by *my* majority. But Hayden interrupted me. Rafael, a Puerto Rican who was an SDS marshal, came rushing in and handed the chairman a note.

"Please sit down." Is he speaking to *me*? My power went, untasted.

"This is an important announcement. We have definite word that there will be a bust before nightfall." I instinctively glanced at the window. Still light. "Anybody who has to leave may leave now. No one will think any less of you if you have to go. It's OK." No one left.

I looked at Terry and shook my head. "I guess this is it," I said. I was frightened for him and for Willie and Brian and Philip and the others, especially for the girls. I had seen the police whip into young demonstrators before—too many times —seen the delight with which they attack. The brutality of their assault almost always corresponded to the youth and weakness of the victim. And the people in the commune were young, most in their late teens and early twenties, and not strong. They would be torn apart and there was nothing I could do to help them when it came, nothing to prevent it, to make it less costly. I could do what I had to do—stand with them, share their hatred and their defeat, witness and work to make those who allowed it to happen pay. This desire for vengeance was my primary response to life in the commune. I had had enough of hostility and injustice. I was ashamed of my country and of its leaders. The rich had grown too rich, the poor too wretched, and it was time to demand an accounting. And if it meant destroying universities, disrupting a nation, if it meant jail and beatings, so be it. I had a deep terror of the police, but my anger was deeper and harder, and when my fear passed—and it usually passed as soon as the cops began to move—only the clean anger remained.

A member of the Legal Committee handed each of us an arraignment form which we filled out. He gave us a telephone number to call if we were isolated from the group and needed a lawyer. I wrote the number on my arm. The head of the Defense Committee stood and showed us the best position to assume if the cops attacked: fall into a fetal position on the ground, arms over your head and neck, legs drawn tightly to the stomach to protect your genitals and internal organs. Then our gas expert (an anarchist from an East Village group called the Motherfuckers) gave us a vivid description of the

125

effects of tear gas and Mace, warning us that if only a small area of the skin is reached by Mace, it can be assimilated by the blood. Thus we were to seal our cuffs with string, put cigarette filters in our nostrils, plastic bags (air holes in the back) over our heads, and use vaseline to close the pores of skin exposed to the air.

The meeting broke up. The passage window on to campus was sealed. Students started collecting bags and filters and gobs of vaseline. We were instructed to disperse ourselves throughout the building, to make it as difficult as possible for the pigs to pull us out. I agreed to meet Terry, Brian, and Roger (lunch bag in hand) in the attic when the cops appeared.

I went into the dining room and made a cup of coffee and sat down on the couch and waited.

About two hours later the news came that the bust was off. It was a false alarm. I was elated by the news of the reprieve. I saw Rebecca, blonde, lovely, tough, and kissed her and said, "Isn't it great! Jesus, I'm glad!" She smiled, "So am I. It'll give us more time to make more clubs." Rebecca, the Irish peasant wife singing her men off to war.

The whole commune was relieved that the bastards had given us more time. And, at the same moment, we were proud of ourselves because no one had walked out, no one had panicked. We had stayed solid. The barricade was taken off the passage window. The singing and dancing started. Someone got a guitar and sat down on the second floor landing and sang Bob Dylan's "It's All Right, Ma." Students sat on the steps before him like a tiered choir and sang along: *though the masters make the rules for the wisemen and the fools, I got nothing, Ma, to live up to.*

About an hour later a bagpiper came into the building and we joined hands in a long chain and danced behind him, snaking through the building, up and down the stairs, playing, shouting happily, singing about how we weren't going

126

to study war no more. And later still I stood with Terry on the balcony beside the red flag in the coolness of that lovely night and tore sheets of paper and threw them down in lieu of rice on the couple who had been married that night in one of the liberated buildings and were walking toward us, now under the balcony, now on the lawn, lighted candles in their hands, a wedding party of tired professors, flower children, and red-banded communards dancing behind them singing. We raised our arms and shouted out into the night: "We've won! We've won!"

Sunday, feeling happy, I went to sleep upstairs on the couch listening to Terry and Mike and Brian talk about how the bust might not come at all, how they were going to hold out until the administration gave in to every demand and if they tried to bust them they would make them regret it. It seemed possible that the demands might be met. There were only six. That the ban on indoor demonstrations be lifted, that the affiliation with the Institute For Defense Analysis (IDA) be ended, the gym stopped, the disciplinary probation against the six students be lifted and that the criminal charges against the students who protested at the gym site and were arrested be dropped, and, finally, that amnesty be given to the students—over one thousand—who occupied the buildings. It was rumored that the administration had secretly given in on all the demands except amnesty and that if we would only hold out, victory would come.

Monday I left campus shortly after noon, going over to the West End Bar—deserted—for lunch and a few drinks. I tried to fortify myself to the task of meeting my parents, returning from their goy First Class Biblical Tour of the Great State of Israel, lunches included. I took a cab out to Kennedy. I felt better about the Columbia Liberation, sure now the bastards would not bust us for at least a few days. I knew the tension was growing. The militants—Roger and Philip among

127

them—had made a pathetic charge against the hundreds of beer-happy jocks lined around Low. Fist fights had broken out. There was a chance that *we* would not wait until the administration acted. It is difficult to live in a tense situation, threatened, swept by rumor, the balance held by your enemies, it is tough when you are young and when you believe deeply that what you are doing is right and necessary. In spite of the growing tension and the threat of a bust—you could taste it in the air—I felt we had won.

I was mistaken.

I went back to the West End Bar, relieved my parents had left New York. It had gone easily, the truth skirted. Our conversation had been limited to Israel and the eighteen led through the artillery-pocked hills into Gethsemane for the service and the sunrise. My duty again would be limited to letters home. No need to justify the lust for violence to them (the politics of cultural despair, Trilling had called it, lifting Fritz Stern's term, a politics where ends had been diminished to the acts themselves), the hatred exhilarating and new, years of guilt and accumulated failure, powerlessness, the ingrown despair released daily like gism in the communes where we reassured ourselves daily of our pacific intent while we panted for the bust. Anything, however violent, to end the growing tension. I did not have to tell them that I was filled with hatred for men and institutions and, yes, for the country I have loved before. In me and in the others I had discovered again a hunger for violence, almost carnal, that admitted no reason. Put the motherfuckers up against the goddamn wall. Them. The cops. The asshole Trustees. The bumbling, duplicitous President. The Middle Class. The Company Students. The Liberal Faculty. Up Against The Wall, Motherfuckers!

"But why?" Mother asked, Israeli-tanned and lovely. "Why get yourself hurt over a bunch of Communists?" She had not

128

read a paper in weeks and already she saw *conspiracy* brooding over the city. She should have been an editor of *The New York Times*. My son the Commie dupe. "For *this* we educate and raise you, for this stealing of buildings and deans?" In her mind the St. Paul papers: LOCAL BOY ARRESTED AS RED AGENT AT COLUMBIA. Revolutions were to be read about, not made, in America. "You part of such a thing? At your age? For this we left *Europe?*"

I had a double scotch at the West End. I wanted to get high before I crawled back into the liberated zone. Math was as dry as an Iowa county, by democratic vote. Who needs it?

It was nearly midnight. The West End was empty of students, except for a few misplaced jocks who usually hung out at the Gold Rail or, failing that, at the Gay Way. Holding the drink in my hand I looked across the bar to the booth where four of them sat dressed like street hustlers in tight shirts and whites and sneakers. Drinking beer. They were out of place here where Ginsberg and Kerouac drank before pot and acid and age and tiredness and fear pressed in on them, drawing them from the world (Ginsberg drunk and bugging Trilling on the phone in the back of the bar . . . *we're both Jews, man, let's admit it*). Time had taken them.

And the Liberation had taken a new generation of Columbia students, leaving in its wake their posturing indifference, their hustling, their cool, their reality, thinning in the smoke that sometimes covered an unadmitted hollowness. And the hippies inside Math, before the Liberation, had fanatically denied the actuality of the future in order to avoid judgment, had rejected political action as a sell-out. These same people, a few days inside the commune, had become obsessed by a Future and its power. Now they crouched inside the occupied Math and Avery and Fayerweather and Low waiting to meet the violence once opposed in the name of Love. Children of the

129

Present, proud of it, hung up on it, now were captives of a Future. William Buckley had once said, archly, dryly, that they wanted to "imminentize the Eschaton." True. The Revolution-To-Come justified everything. All had become judgmental.

The West End was strangely quiet. Smokeless. It made me uncomfortable. The air there is usually unbreatheable, but Monday night, emptied of heads and drunks spilling urine on the bathroom floors, and old ladies, and students crowded over beers, the air was clean. I could not get high. And I wanted to in order to confront Hayden in the name of Moderation and Reason. That was my bag. Worry over friends, puffed by detachment, conservatizes. But I was so politically untrained that I had to have a few drinks to convince myself I was winning him when, if ice sober, I would see I was losing miserably. All was politics. Even the West End, like the University and the community, drooped with thick rhetoric, smelled of politics. Joyless. "All within the Revolution," Hayden had declared, half-facetiously, the age not weighing yet the resurrected terms, the retread revolutions of the East. It was still 1825 in twentieth-century America by Hayden's calendar. And he worked to press the year with decades.

The bartender asked me if I had seen Rafael. I told him he was in Math. "He owes me money," he said, "the filthy spic."

Even Rafael had changed. Somehow he found a grim sort of manhood, contingent though it was, situationalist, separate but equal, in darting between the communes playing Professional Puerto Rican to the whites. We listened. The blacks did not. No whites or spics welcome in Malcolm X (Hamilton) Hall.

Rafael's rhetoric was limited to a hoarse but well-meant "I am for *my* America, whitey, after we burn *your* America to the fucking ground!" Effective, especially when he delivered his speech with his greatcoat thrown over his shoulders and his

130

red armband glistening below his clenched fist. It was pretense, though it was delivered with such ease in telling that it made his past dissolve one week, and fiction grew inside his mind, stretching his revolutionary past back beyond last Friday to Lenin—this Puerto Rican pimp—back to Herzin and Belinsky—this pusher, pornographer, pimp—back to where his memory was lost to names and race and all violence took the name of Freedom. As I drank in the West End he was over in Math, his greatcoat discarded on the fifth floor, playing revolutionary general to the whites. Outwardly cool. His stomach tight. Feeling less white as the cops moved on to campus. "How does a black cop feel clubbing us?" Willie asked Rafael. "It makes him feel white," he had replied on Sunday.

The Liberation had taken Rafael with the rest. I remembered the joints bought, the speed. I remembered the night in his pad at 124th, his old lady in the kitchen with her Gallo, a lighted candle before the saint on the wall stand, San Juan beaches nearing in the wine. Rafael pinned a sheet to the wall and, at five bucks a head, I and Terry and Brian watched blue movies, Cuban export. Dogs fucking women. Men eating each other. Old men eating little girls. During each flick his old lady wandered into the room, looked a minute and mumbled in Spanish that she had seen it, cursed and wandered out. And now Rafael was donning grease, a shield, his face too dark, and waiting for the bust. A prison record. Would the bastards give him bail?

It was twelve-thirty. I ordered another drink. When the bartender slid it across the bar to me he said low, "They get those red punks tonight."

"Who does?"

"You haven't seen it? Christ, they're piling out of buses on Amsterdam. Looks like a goddamn army camp over there."

Tonight. Impossible. We are negotiating. They promised. Negotiate and no bust. "Are you sure?"

"Dead certain. It's for real this time. The fucking punks!"

For real. I left quickly. Outside and cool, a light breeze coming over the Hudson from the west. I remembered walking with Al along the Drive. Now fear tasted in my mouth, so soon, so soon, as I ran across Broadway toward the 116th Street gates. I had to get back inside Math. I belonged there. All I could think of as I ran was the fear that I would arrive too late, that before I could reach the entrance window into Math the blood already would have won. My friends. Terry, who thinks like a poet, and Brian, who laughs at violence and believes, and Willie . . . Crazy Mike . . . Rebecca . . . Rebecca who made the clubs and got the gasoline . . . they'll be cut apart, the fucking walls washed with them, bled over the floors, along the steps, broken.

At the gates, "I've got to get on campus!" I showed my ID card.

"The campus is closed. Move or face arrest."

"This is important! I'm part of the Math commune. My friends are there. I *belong* there!" Goddamn asslicking cops. "Move!"

I moved. Up Broadway, trying to circle the campus at 120th and over to the Amsterdam gates. The shouting of the crowds inside the campus was starting, my fear pushing like a hard knot in my chest. Running I pictured my head being clubbed by eight-foot-tall cops, swaddled in shiny leather, bulging, and my brain damaged . . . years later my limping dramatically through Leftist assemblies, people awed and drunk with sweet pity—the Martyr!—as I, a one-man Abraham Lincoln Brigade, stumbled half-wittedly through the crowd, a Crippled Veteran of the Columbia Rebellion.

Two horse vans were lined along 120th Street, across from Teachers College and Union Theological Seminary. Horses filled the street. Twenty or so uniformed cops, smug in leather, tall, tough, strutting like leather queens on Christopher Street,

132

their hands itching to swing, to prove manhood again and again. Jogging by them, I instinctively put my hand in my pocket and covered my cock protectively. The smell of manure and piss, the smell that would cling to Broadway and the walks for days after, was there in the street. Fresh blood has no smell.

I reached Amsterdam Avenue. There, along the walls of Columbia, hundreds of cops stood in line facing the street waiting. Five, ten city buses marked SPECIAL, filled with sadistic plainclothesmen looking like bouncers from dockside bars, or pimps . . . cops in other buses . . . cops inside the gates, hundreds . . . cops belching and itching to kill, leaning butch under the ledges above which Trilling and Quentin Anderson and Steve Marcus wrote . . . police vans, paddy wagons, two ambulances, police cars, red lights playing on the University buildings, reflecting on the windows of Philosophy Hall where the Ad Hoc Faculty Group had argued and lost, where the wounded were taken that night. Crowds of whites packed across the street from the gates, along the walls under the Law Bridge, jeering the cop pigs . . . fascist motherfuckers . . . and where was Harlem? Two old colored ladies— one screaming hysterically at the cops, "You's evil! You's evil!"; the other knocking over a litter basket and kicking it toward the cops. Futile anger. Harlem was asleep.

No entrance. Closed. A cop at the gates jabbed a billy club hard into my stomach. Move! Breathless. I ran to 114th and over to Broadway again, west of the fenced gym site over which press and administration and students fought to avoid the meaning of the fight. On Broadway three ABC cameramen were laughing as they talked. The noise from the campus grew louder. The shouting built and faded and built again. "Kill 'em!" came from the jocks gathered at Low. The bust was still to come.

Near the Broadway gates I saw a professor I knew. I went

133

up to him and told him I had to get on campus. He understood.

Professor Dodson was an hour away, told the bust was called off, two drinks later, driving toward Sparkill . . . Trilling was home exhausted . . . One professor was in front of Hamilton renewing the Thirties and his credentials as a man . . . Dean Platt was home . . . the President and the Vice President were held in the basement of Low listening to Captain Denesco reassure them of the cops' professionalism . . . in Fayerweather the barricades were being checked once more and the commune reminded of its pledge to non-violence . . . the cops were moving on to Low silently . . . the captain raising his bullhorn, "In the name of the Trustees of Columbia University I order . . ." The blacks had given in in Hamilton, led like sheep by the cops through tunnels into paddy wagons, like Jews moved into the showers, Al among them, Al among them . . . Avery was pulling on plastic bags . . . in Mathematics the students were in the middle of their anti-gas preparations and one boy, seventeen, was sobbing out his fear in the second-floor bathroom. It was an hour to the bust.

The professor and I walked to the gates. The cop barricades were in place. A junior faculty member was in charge. He stopped us.

"No one admitted. The gates are closed." He sounded very official, smug, enjoying his power as gatekeeper.

"Do you know who I am?"

"Yes, Professor. But no one is to be admitted."

"I'm going through and he is coming with me."

The gatekeeper glanced nervously at the police a few feet away. Television lights lit the gates. "I can't, sir."

"Do you want tenure at this university?"

He let us through.

On College Walk, just before I darted up the steps toward Mathematics, the professor grabbed my arm and stopped me.

"Why, Dotson, why all this coming violence, this playing at revolution?"

I looked at him carefully. He had spoken with great sadness, almost out of defeat, and I was moved by the concern expressed in his voice. His face, the pain of it, reminded me of Lowell. "I guess because we are trying to make the world safe for our friends. At least I am. And I don't know any other way."

I ran up the steps. He called out behind me. "Protect yourself!"

The crowds of angry students were being shoved by the cops away from Low Library to the steps of Earl Hall. They were militant and loud, shouting at the cops. The plainclothesmen had begun their deadly infiltration of the crowds, some of them dressed like students, carrying books. On College Walk cops were trooping on to campus, vans and paddy wagons lined from Kent to Dodge Halls. Over Alma Mater's head someone had fixed a sign that read: RAPED BY THE COPS. I heard screaming in the distance and shouts that echoed through the quads across the lawns. The commune had begun to take up the defiant slogan, hurling it at the cops from the windows and roofs: UP AGAINST THE WALL MOTHERFUCKERS.

I stood on the grass in front of Math begging admission. The building was sealed. I shouted up to the windows, cupping my hands over my mouth, "I'm with you, baby, all the way!" They shouted back encouragement.

I got in front of Mathematics and leaned against the glass doors behind which tables and chairs and pathetic board barricades were built for defense. Only the barricades and the bodies of us before the door stood between the cops and the commune.

I stood before the doors, linking arms with four other young men, all of us frightened, all beginning to sweat. In front of us another line. And in front of that three professors, one with white hair, a tiny man. That was all the army of faculty—liberal, boasting that they would never allow the cops on their campus, we will stand by you, before you, behind you—that was all the army of faculty that bothered to appear before Math. We held each other's arms and waited. Paul, at the end of my line, started screaming hysterically at the cops as they came by the hundreds through the Earl Hall gates around the side of Math and another contingent came to us across from Low Library. As they assembled in long, tight lines before us, hundreds of them facing nine young men and three old men barring their entrance, as they grouped and waited, it seemed for hours, unmoving, the tension mounting, Paul yelled, "Motherfucking, cocksucking bastard cops! Fascists! Fascists!" over and over again. I glanced over at him and shrugged. His face was flushed, his hair wet with sweat. He had not shaved in five days and he looked tired and drawn. He was eighteen. And he looked utterly terrified and defiant and beautiful to me as he screamed his outrage against the fucking liberal world. The white-haired professor, after Paul had gone on for awhile, broke ranks and went up to him. "Son," he said quietly, his hand on Paul's shoulder, "You're showing your fear. Calm yourself. We're all together. Those fascist animals will have to get through us to get to you. And I'll wear the bastards out." Paul quieted down.

I took out my contact lenses and put them in their case and shoved it in my pocket. I took off my tie to prevent strangulation. Then I waited with my friends while behind me, beguilingly, magnificently, my friends, those brave and sad young men, shouted into the night: UP AGAINST THE WALL MOTHERFUCKERS. The cry was taken up by other buildings and by the crowds and carried into the darkness.

A man in a tan trench coat stood about fifteen feet before us and said into a bullhorn: "In the name of the Trustees of Columbia University I order you to leave. . . ."

They came at us fast and hard. The three professors were moved out quickly. Then the line of students in front of us folded quickly, some of them knocked to the ground. They were dragged away. Then the motherfucking pigs reached us. The boys at each end of the line braced themselves against the building. We held our arms tightly, legs spread, heads down. They kicked our legs and stomachs trying to make us break. We held for several minutes until the bastards took each of us by the hair and yanked us apart. I was thrown to the ground, kicked in the stomach, and then lifted by two plainclothesmen and thrown ten feet over the hedges onto the lawns. When I tried to get up they kicked me down. Two cops, each grabbing a leg, dragged me down the Earl Hall steps and ordered me to wait. Then Paul was dragged out. After a while we stood and ran down Broadway, the cops chasing us about a block. The motherfuckers.

While I was being pulled off campus the cops were making their way into the building, pulling the furniture out of the doorway and throwing it on the lawns. It took them fifteen minutes to clear the building; rope and hoses held the barricades in place. They were met by six boys sitting, arms locked, on the soaped stairs. They were arrested. Then Hayden and a few others were pulled out.

After the first floor was cleared, the cops went from room to room methodically axing down every door, smashing furniture and walls, beating kids, pulling them along the stone stairways face down, their heads leaving blood smeared like thin paint along the steps.

At 114th Street I climbed over the Ferris Booth gate and jumped back on to campus. Paddy wagons filled with students were being driven out College Walk, crowds of students on the lawns shouting their solidarity at the fucking cops: UP AGAINST THE WALL MOTHERFUCKERS!

The plainclothesmen started to clear South Field of thousands of students milling in rage, viciously driving them like frightened deer, trapping them between buildings and police, moving them in terror one way and then another, playing with them, dropping like animals on top of them when they fell—three, four plainclothes cops to each of the fallen students.

I was driven out of campus with the main contingent of students, several thousand of us running from the police to Broadway, there to be met by mounted police. The horsemen drove into us as we flooded into the street, crushing some of us against the gates and the sides of buildings.

I broke ranks and ran past a score of cops down Broadway to Furnald Hall. The French windows were open. I shouted, "I'm coming in!" and I climbed the grating to the ledge and fell into the dormitory lounge, my ass being clubbed by a cop as I went inside. I saw Doug, a friend of mine, and we collected liquor from the rooms for the infirmaries in Philosophy and Ferris Booth Halls.

Then Doug and I climbed four flights and stood on the upper ledge of Furnald, the windows filled with angry students shouting at the fucking cops, and looked down Broadway. My chest constricted with anger and impotence, hating the cops and the goddamn administration and the half-assed president and the cocksucking University itself, and hating—patriotically, cleanly—America. Hating her fucking cops and troopers and her ways and manners and indifference, her lack of human sentiment and kindness, her arrogance, her pious, *Christian* people who justified violence and spread death over the earth. Doug, his young, strong face contorted in anger, his body tense with rage, started yelling obscenities at the cops. And I, hatred breaking me, joined his rage: UP AGAINST THE WALL MOTHERFUCKERS. ASSLICKING FASCIST FAGGOT COPS. PIMPS. GODDAMN CUNTEATING CORRUPT BASTARDS. My imagination dead, I clung to the epithet, "bastard," and hurled it monotonously, repet-

138

itively, at the cops. We threw empty beer cans and lighted cigarettes down on them as they herded the terrified students up and down Broadway, allowing them no exit, whipping them with clubs, driving them into walls, making them fall again and again to be kicked and pummeled and arrested. I spit at them, shouted, hating them—and if I could I would have edged my ass over the avenue and dropped my hatred and my disgust on my America with her child-beating fascist cops and bloody, senseless wars, with her hypocritical, deadly leaders, her lack of compassion, her endless racism and inbred hatred, her balling, imperialist violence; America the violent, the disreputable, the outrageous, the incestuous land, devouring her children, feeding us bile and hunger for death; my unhappy America, my pathetic, stupid, bloody country, self-righteous and vicious, my evil land beating her sons and daughters, killing her young men in useless wars, exploiting her weak, making victims of the young and poor and powerless; my country, led by fools and asslicking Company Men who terrorize the earth. America, how I hated you that night and how clean and good and redemptive that hatred was.

Around six-thirty Tuesday morning I walked back inside Mathematics. Empty. The floors and walls wet. I climbed the stairs. Blood smears on the walls. Broken glasses. Single shoes. Pieces of torn clothing. Bloody clumps of hair.

The place had been vandalized by the police. Ink thrown against the walls. Papers strewn everywhere. Furniture and doors and walls destroyed by axes and crowbars.

I went into the attic. "Who's there?" someone asked. I stopped, standing under the light. "It's Dotson. I'm part of the Math commune."

Roger came out from behind a partition, his lunch bag in hand. "God, you should've seen it. It was unbelievable. Oh, the fucking bastards, the bastards!"

139

"How did you escape?"

"I climbed out the window in the roof and hung over the side by my hands until they left. The fucking bastards. Somebody's got to pay for what they've done. Somebody's got to pay."

chapter ten

WHEN SOMETHING TERRIBLE HAPPENS IN A FAMILIAR
place, when violence or death intrudes massively, the place
itself becomes foreign to what it was. It becomes something
other. It becomes unpredictable.

Columbia. After the bust. The buildings and lawns, the
Thinker green before Philosophy, the Van Am quad, the
sundial, the fountains before Low, the entire place seemed
different, unknown, as if I were arriving there for the first
time. It meant something new. No one, not even the police
and administrators who planned it, not the Mayor who tried
to stop it, the faculty who worked to avoid it, the jocks and
alumni who sought to make it happen, not the radical and
moderate students in the buildings, not Tom Hayden, not
even the SDS Steering Committee who saw in confrontation
the promise of a wider revolt, precursor of revolution, triumphant, no one really believed it would be as bloody and
insane as it was. No one, not even the blood-high cops who
wielded the clubs—generations of lawlessness webbed too long,
nascent criminality, blood lust letting go—nor the kids and
profs beaten, no one before the event expected it to happen
as it did. That does not mitigate the responsibility of those
complicit in the violence but it does explain the pall that
came over the campus, the sense of disbelief and terror (un-

boundedness—anything could happen now) that we felt that morning. Unease. Cops everywhere, lounging like an occupation army in the lobbies of the dorms, eating in the student cafeterias, milling around Low, sitting on the steps of the chapel, as self-conscious in our presence as we were in theirs, wary of each other, walking in twos and threes around campus, patroling College Walk, in large black-leathered packs on South Field. Smug like Presbyterian ushers, lawanorder their bag. Better than sex. *Officially* Righteous.

Late morning. A freshman climbed the flagpole in front of Low and tried to lower the University's flag to half mast. His *flag*. And the cops, the new proprietors, the University belonging more to them than to us—it had become property, a piece of New York real estate—resenting us as only second-generation immigrants' sons can, sons who do not find the golden roads, the American Money Dream beyond the freedom that brought their fathers breathless to this shore, resenting the luxury of our years, the expense of our education, the nimbus of an ordained future in the System given off like gas by the soon-to-be-held degree, resenting ultimately the contempt we had for the System. How deeply hate festers, born of envy. And what they envied we despised. That morning. The cops, seeing the boy climb the flagpole, rushed at him nightsticks in hand, pulled him down, clubbed him and dragged him into Low. And four of us, *compatriots*, classmates no longer, followed several feet behind shouting PIG! PIG! Absurd. Then we spied the Proctor of the University, William Kahn, a small, lumpish man, gray-haired, good-humored, fair, undoubtedly wanting to keep the job he had recently won, friendly to young men, seeing him we ran up and broke our anger and frustration on him. "Who are these bastards . . . who are these fucking cops . . . these pigs to discipline on this campus, these ignorant louts (despite our protested radicalism, inside pitted against the skull the intellectual elitism of being at Columbia. A privileged class, the game turned against us, we demanded our favors. They may have the guns and power but we had the brains. We were the chosen ... Rah. Rah. It meant nothing anymore. Being a student at the University no longer offered asylum, protection on campus, in the buildings. One was safer in the streets. We had been disowned and we were of two minds about it), who the hell are these bastards to take that kid away?"

"What kid?" Kahn asked bewildered.

"The kid ... there was a student trying to lower the flag half mast and the fuckers clubbed him and pulled him into Low!"

"So?"

"Do something! You're supposed to *help* us [aristocrats insisting on our prerogatives], *do* something!"

"But what can I do?" Honest, as helpless as we were. But we wanted other than honesty. We wanted protection. Our rights!

"Go in after him! Get him released."

Poor Kahn. He liked us and wanted to help but he hesitated. He tried to move away declaring his non-involvement, but we were angry as hell. The only administration figure to appear in the open and we were mad enough to beat the shit out of him.

"Go in, goddamn it! Go in!"

Still he procrastinated. The four of us got behind him and literally pushed him to the entrance of Low.

We waited outside, pissed, angry, bitching at the University, talking loudly of retaking the damn buildings after the cops left that night, burning the place to the ground (the cops never left).

About twenty minutes later Kahn came out, success beaming across his face. The freshman was walking in front of him, head lowered. Kahn brought him to us. We were standing on the steps near the fountain.

"Tell them," Kahn said.

The kid looked up at us, frightened.

"What? Tell us what?" Brian asked, indignant. Something was wrong.

"You know," Kahn coached. "Tell them what you promised."

The boy looked down, nervous, shaking, he seemed scared and ashamed.

"I want to apologize for pulling down the flag ... it was wrong ... for being ... for being in the liberated buildings ... that was wrong, too." He looked at Kahn. "Is that enough?"

Kahn, sheepish (he did not like his job anymore): "Sure. I guess so."

"What'd you say that for?" Brian asked the boy. And then suspecting the truth, "Did they make you say that, did the bastards make you?"

The boy nodded that they had. Kahn moved away, and as he did he said, "Now you all be good. You go on home. Get some sleep." For once he reminded me of a Southern café owner in Maryland. Not wanting trouble. Wanting to be *liked*, please, to be liked.

"What'd they do?" Brian asked the boy.

"The cops hit me ... (he was starting to cry and trying not to, so he coughed and stammered to cover it, to save his masculinity. Boys do not cry in America) and one of them kneed me in the balls. In Low ... right in front of Barzun's office. Right there ... I fell down and they said they'd arrest me and beat the shit out of me if I didn't come out and apologize ... and then they laughed."

Right in front of Jacques Barzun's office. There was the University inside behind the door while the young were getting kneed in the balls by the cops. Typical. The President and Vice President downstairs in Low while the pigs were mopping up their students ("All our sons," Arthur Miller once asserted in another generation's sentiment). Nice old men. Teachers, Bastards.

Just before noon, so drawn out and tired that I was beyond feeling, I walked into Livingston Hall (dormitory) and showed the room key to the cop at the door. Showed him my I.D. He checked. Double-checked. Told him who the President of the University was. Who my adviser was. Finally the cop let me through.

I used the key and went into Willie's room (Willie had given me a key when the Liberation began so I could stay in the dorm in case the campus was sealed). With my clothes on —man, I smelled five days bathless—I climbed into the top bunk and fell asleep.

chapter eleven

IMMEDIATELY AFTER THE BUST A STUDENT STRIKE
was declared. It was supported by the great majority of the
student body and by most of the faculty. The demands of the
strike were the six original which had led to the Liberation,
plus the demand that Kirk and Truman must resign. I do not
believe that most of the students and faculty who supported
the strike did so necessarily because they agreed with all the
demands. Rather the strike—and it was effective in closing
down the undergraduate divisions until the year ended—grew
out of a general sense of outrage and an awareness of the need
for radical reform. The administration, in refusing to accede
to the original demands and in bringing in the police to break
the Liberation, had radicalized the faculty and the moderate
students and polarized the University community against itself. The original demands now seemed moderate in the new
context and the administration (the kind of administration
which could bloody heads and then not comprehend its own
mistake) plus the use of police to resolve an internal University dispute became the primary issues.

The University ceased to be a unified, functioning human
community and the institution floundered amid an escalation
of rhetoric and passion, administration, faculty and students
divided into warring factions among themselves, every god-

damn thing taking on enormous political importance. Friendships of many years were dissolved. Distrust, jealousy, the fueling of bitterness spread. The administration no longer enjoyed the allegiance of the majority. The fact that violence could come to Columbia (and who knew when to expect it again?), that reasoned debate, compromise, orderly processes of resolution—all the liberal procedural verities—could not prevent the police attack led most of the University to consider the institution, as it was presently constituted, illegitimate. It was no longer worthy of loyalty. Loyalty transferred from the administration and the official legal bodies to groupings of interests. The faculty and students saw themselves as entities separate from the administration and, in a historical and educational if not legal sense, superior to it. They *were* the University. Regardless of the legal sanction behind the Trustees, for us they ceased to hold the University in trust. Columbia belonged to us.

These feelings of ownership over the University, of solidarity with each other, of commitment to restructuring the institution, this sense of place and belonging was the most beautiful and remarkable aspect of the post-Liberation days. The institution had been built and administratively structured in such a way as to prevent the creation of community and loyalty to groups within the community itself. Unlike the great majority of American universities, there was no unified faculty at Columbia. The faculty was divided into four Faculties, and the professional schools constituted separate kingdoms apart from the liberal arts faculties. One had the sense that each group of faculty, each school, was fighting against the others for attention from the administration and for a bigger piece of the pie.

And the students (particularly the undergraduates) got the shaft. No one respected their interests. New money went to the professional schools (Business, Law, International Affairs, etc.). They were the ones who received the new buildings, the expanded faculties. Undergraduate education was neglected. The students were poorly housed, poorly fed, generally ignored except at payment time. And they, like the Senateless faculty, were denied any sort of central government with which to press the administration. In addition the students, again like the faculty, were divided into several camps—General Studies, the College, Barnard, Engineering, the Graduate divisions, the professional schools—and thus were unable to act as one body. They were not aware of their common interests and they, like their professors, tended to be jealous of each other—the College sniping at General Studies, the graduate students undercutting the undergraduates.

And alone, far above the quarrel, the administration looked on playing the sides against each other, growing arrogant. While practically and immediately it was the students who were most hurt by the faculty/student divisions, it was the administration who in the long run suffered the most. Kirk simply did not know what was going on at the University. Surrounded by toadies, removed, never coming into actual contact with the life of the institution, he could not recognize the symptoms of malfunction as they appeared. Certainly by the beginning of the academic year, nearly nine months before the Liberation, it was obvious to most teachers (as opposed to research hacks) and radical students that Columbia was set up for a massive disruption. Not even after the bust was Kirk convinced of the extreme danger of the situation. He would not admit that the University had changed radically. He kept up with business as usual (and to him that was precisely what it was—business) refusing to recognize the severe change in attitude which occurred on campus after the Liberation was crushed.

Several hours after the bust I spoke with one of the deans. I asked him when Kirk was going to resign. "Kirk resign?" he said, astonished. "Are you kidding? To do that would be to admit to all their demands. No, Kirk will never resign. We'll

ride this thing out. Exams are coming. Things will cool off."
(He was as bad a prophet as he was an administrator.)

The situation then was the progressive estrangement of the
academic (student/faculty) sectors of the University from
the administrative (administration plus Trustees) center
coupled with the radicalization of formerly moderate factions.
The administration and the Trustees were hated and distrusted. The estrangement took actual form in the refusal of
teachers and students to meet in assigned classrooms in Columbia buildings (property under the legal control of the Trustees). Instead, classes were held in professors' apartments, off-
campus rooms, parks and on the lawns. By these acts the
students and faculty were saying that a university is not property but it is people and without us Columbia ceases to exist.
It was perhaps a simpleminded notion but it was a tremen-
dously attractive one. We embraced it. We withdrew. We
demanded amnesty. We demanded justice.

During the weeks after the Liberation I spent my time
sitting in on classes on the lawns or picketing before classroom
buildings and sometimes Willie or Sophie or Philip sat with
me and Rudd or Rafael or someone else would come along
checking, giving us encouragement, telling us about a noon
rally to be held or about police stationed in some new place
on campus. We tended to stay in groups, for the cops were
now a part of our lives. Everywhere. The Liberation smashed
and the administration had admitted a new class, the cops,
who were more welcomed by them on campus than we had
ever felt. God knows.

During this period a kind of deadlock developed between
all the parties. The administration sat aloof, denying in optimistic press releases the actual effectiveness of the strike.
The faculty attempted to organize itself. It met twice as one
body—the Joint Faculties—and appointed an Executive Committee, one member of which was Trilling. The students also
organized themselves into a Strike Committee which tried to

maintain pressure on the administration in order to win the demands. During this time vast amounts of information, previously unavailable to the community, fell into SDS hands. Information about University holdings, future plans, associations with Defense Department research and the use of honorary degrees and faculty appointments by the State Department to further American foreign policy objectives. One case in point was the granting of an honorary degree to Queen Frederika of Greece during a period when she was under renewed attack in Greece for her alleged collaboration with the Nazis during the war. The State Department believed that a Columbia doctorate would give her additional prestige in Greece and help to stabilize the nation.

Dinner time. The day after the bust. I went down to the Lion's Den in Ferris Booth for a hamburger. Like most students I tried to stay on campus as much as possible because the place was sealed and one never knew when the kind or amount of evidence needed for entrance would change. I went into the Lion's Den—typical in its bad food and high prices of most of the campus cafeterias established for student use—and sitting in the near corner at a booth was Hayden. Man, I could have cried. Right there I could have broken down sobbing I was so goddamn happy to see his acne-scarred face, his narrow, dark eyes, his beauty. All of it—the days arguing in the liberated lounges, the nights of bad sleep in the faculty offices, the hopeless sex, the sheer loveliness of solidarity, the terror when the troopers came rushing, rushing, Paul's yell, the clubbing, the redundant violence—the week of the Liberation rose in me at seeing Tom, filled me with sentiment close to love, like high school nostalgia (an American vice) waves into one when you are a freshman in college away from home and some popular song from high school years is played and you miss, *miss* what is gone and will not come back, miss it because no more are you fitted to live it, gone beyond, passed over, grown. Hayden. He stood for all of it. He played our hearts, buoyed our courage, dragged us into ourselves discovering strength and rage and citizenship ignited bursting—and what else? Darker, more deadly, the thirst for dissolution and the end of things. Mild, Tom.

He had come from Newark with his Community Union Project—a failure—trying to steel the blacks against centuries of defeat and in defeat won himself. He *became* Tom Hayden. His own. Long way to come, friend, in time and distance and belief from Oak Park, Michigan, near Detroit, and the Shrine of Our Lady of the Little Flower and the America Firsters' priest, mute and bitter under the Bishop's seal. Catholic. His father an accountant. Nun-taught. From there to the University of Michigan, into SDS, working with the Civil Rights Movement in the South, escaping barely with his life. Married. Divorced. Running diplomat to Hanoi, two, three trips to North Vietnam, twice bringing American prisoners back with him. Gentle, Tom. To us legend. What we wanted to be. Modest. Wanting power—compulsive—but wanting it with a style beyond offense. I and the others in the Math commune would have followed like children did the Piper, followed him into violence and beyond, knowing finally he was indifferent to our fate—the Second America unborn, midwife to it, transcending us and him. Remorseless, obsessed, as no other man I have ever met (save Billy Graham), by a vision of what was to come. A dangerous madness his. Hayden. Seeing him there munching hamburgers I missed him, loved him and I wanted—I'll admit it—to be taken away by him, for where he was the Revolution grew. He was *in* history. At twenty-eight. I wanted to go away with him, to be beckoned. Poor Tom, to bear such fool's loyalty from so many students. To carry so goddamn much on his back. To be watched and mimicked and emulated and misunderstood.

"Jesus! Tom, it's so goddamn great to see you!" I gushed (yes, friends, *gushed*), running over. He stretched out his hand and smiled, his mouth full of food, and indicated that I was to sit.

I pulled a chair up near to him. One of the students at his table was talking revolutionary theory and Tom was listening, interested but uninvolved. The other students at the table resented my coming. Whoever wanted to share him? Shit, not me.

"When are we taking the buildings again?" I asked him, laying particular emphasis on the pronoun.

"I don't know," he said, cocking his head toward me, grinning. "When are you taking the buildings again?"

"Tonight!" I said, wanting to boast for him, wishing there were a cop in the place to walk up to and slug with Hayden looking on. But there wasn't. There never is when you need one.

He bent his head to the side, his eyebrows arched, skeptical. "Hold off for awhile," he said, "at least until I leave." I did not know whether he was teasing me or not.

"Leave?" Lonely already.

"Back to Chicago. Tonight. I got other places to go. It's a big country and a lot to do."

Smack! I was wiped out. "But we *need* you," I implored. And then I felt embarrassed because it was not strong and I wanted very badly to be strong in front of him.

"No, you don't. Not anymore." He smiled. Columbia was in a day's work. The University had been radicalized, polarized, brought to a halt. We had all changed because of what we had experienced. But he was beyond change. The mountain top, baby, where Martin King stood before Memphis, that is where he was at. And we were moving like him, toward him. He was right. We did not need him anymore.

chapter twelve

THE STRIKE CONTINUED THROUGH MAY.

On May 16th the administration began to set the stage for confrontation. Kirk had learned nothing. Neck-deep in the Big Muddy, the big fool said to push on. The administration sent letters to Rudd and four other SDS leaders, all on disciplinary probation, ordering them to appear in the Dean's Office on May 21 before 5 P.M. No reason was given for their appearance.

These five students, in addition to nearly a thousand others, faced criminal charges resulting from arrests made on the night of the bust. The Joint Committee on Discipline (a faculty body) had recommended that there be no academic discipline until the criminal charges were dropped (their recommendation) or the court proceedings concluded. It was a surprise then when Kirk picked the five SDS leaders for disciplinary action. In so doing he went directly against the stated ruling of the faculty. Discipline against the five would lead to their immediate expulsion from the University and, more importantly, it would prejudice their criminal trials.

At about four in the afternoon on May 21, SDS held a rally at the sundial. After Rudd and several others spoke, about four hundred students walked to Hamilton Hall, joined by the parents of the five summoned students, to wait in the lobby while the lawyers for the five informed the Dean that the students—on their advice—would not appear before him. At least not until after their court trials.

The students in the lobby were generally in a good, if not hopeful, mood. We were together again and we were there to witness our leaders standing up to the Dean. While we waited, several hundred more students gathered outside.

Dean Platt (a decent man. He was better than his job. The administration would make it impossible for him to stay before the summer came) met with the parents and the lawyers. Nothing was resolved. He told the lawyers that if the students failed to appear they would be immediately expelled. It seemed unfair. Dean Platt agreed to call his superior, Acting Dean Coleman, and request a meeting. On the phone Dean Coleman said he would meet the parents at nine that night. Dean Platt came out and told us of the rescheduled meeting. He told us to stay calm, that things would work out all right. Most students trusted Dean Platt—during the Liberation he was the only administration official welcomed around Math—because he had a cool, almost upper-class English sense of fair play. He was a good man, open, interested, young—I think he was in his early thirties—and fascinated by the very radicalism which disturbed him, the disaffection which he knew unacknowledged. I know he did not agree with the tactics we had used but he understood our reasons. He *felt* for us. He tried to walk the strait line, holding our trust; but Kirk, calling in all the cards for one last spectacular deal, had him by the balls, and before the night was done Dean Alexander Platt, like the students who taxed his concern, would get Kirk's well-aimed shaft.

While we waited in the lobby Acting Dean Coleman was in Low Library with President Kirk and Vice President Truman.

While the three met, we milled around the lobby of Hamilton and waited for word from the Dean. Since the building did not close until ten o'clock we were in no violation of University regulations, however, Dean Coleman shortly arrived and warned us to leave.

About eight o'clock Dean Coleman came into Hamilton Hall again, under his short-cropped hair his gray face for once pink with sweet power. He told us that the students had been suspended. There would be no more meetings, contrary to what Dean Platt had announced. Furthermore he said: "As an officer of the University [how goddamn beautiful those words—*officer of the University*—must have sounded to him. In the club at last. The power!] I have no alternative [a lie, but an easy one] but to call the police if you do not leave. Any student arrested will be suspended for an indefinite period [in direct contradiction of the Joint Committee's procedures for due process]."

His job done, the Acting Dean went back to Kirk to report. The President called a news conference and announced that there was to be no violence, they had no desire for violence, God knows, no desire at all—and then waited for the troops to come.

After the Acting Dean left there was some discussion as to what to do. We all believed that the arrests would be symbolic—non-violent—and therefore many of us left.

The crowds on campus grew as the word spread that the cops were coming. Again. I wandered around, meeting Willie on the upper campus, and we went downstairs into Lewisohn Hall (the General Studies building across from Low) and had a Coke and a sandwich. We were convinced that the bust would be relatively easy, that the University would not try to replay the April bust, that the cops would not come in massive force.

As we sat talking the police began to assemble on the perimeters of the campus, the press arrived, the plainclothesmen, the mounted police. It was happening again.

Around eleven o'clock plainclothesmen started to infiltrate the campus, coming in groups. At 2 A.M. the bust began. Some

155

plainclothesmen, rushing the schedule, began attacking several girls on the South Field. A crowd formed and chased them off campus. Victory for our side.

About the same time the cops began sneaking through the tunnels under Hamilton. The building was busted.

As the Hamilton Hall students were being taken, Willie and I were on the Engineering Terrace, north of Low. There were several hundred other students in the immediate area because in the courtyard below, off Amsterdam Avenue, police and patrol cars stood waiting in large numbers. We assumed that they constituted the main body of police and that the arrested students would be brought there or out nearby Schermerhorn Hall. We started to yell obscenities down at the cops. They ignored us except to raise their middle fingers or to shout "Fuck you!" at us. On the whole it was a good-natured exchange. But as we waited and the students failed to appear and more cops came and sounds of screaming came from the South Lawns and rumors spread of beatings, as the time passed we grew nervous and tense, the hatred brewing, the thought of the first bust on our minds. And we were angered because there seemed no reason for cops being on campus. We had staged no demonstration against the rules in Hamilton. There had been no trouble.

While we waited on the Terrace, students were building barricades at the Amsterdam and Broadway gates to keep the cops off campus. They used wooden horses and litter baskets and wide sheets of metal.

About a half an hour after I arrived on the Engineering Terrace a student came running up. "The pigs are on campus! They're beating people on South Field!" Just then about six plainclothesmen appeared at the doors to the Business School. They grabbed a student standing near the front doors and started beating him up. The kid yelled. Maybe thirty or more students left the Terrace and ran to his aid. The plainclothes cops fled.

156

That act of brutality sent us wild. Something slipped in our minds, cracked, and the rage broke through, spilling over us. We hated everything! Hell, everyone in authority, power, those who eat the earth. The first-class professional bastards.

It came over us, like a kind of freedom, openness, and we gave way and fell to our outrage and struck back. Pathetically. Unarmed. Against the wall.

We dropped cement flower pots and cement sign bases and bricks from the walks on the patrol cars below. We spit at the cops and shouted—again—UP AGAINST THE WALL MOTHERFUCKERS. Back in the core of it, near America's heart, touching the clit of her lust, her true nature, *cops!* Hayden was right. We didn't need him anymore. It was our fight. Cops! Administrators! Old Men! Cops! Politicians! Cops! Trustees! Cops! Cops! America—nothing but waves, hordes, packs of fucking bluebottles, pigs, club-swinging, violence-doped, redneck, fascist *cops!* Everywhere. All the time. America and her cops. Christ! Infested by cops.

We gave way. I did, hating again, in love with it, in the pit of my being, washed with the anguish and endless defeat, mixed with it, years of being terror-struck by redneck cops in the South in Washington in Boston in Minneapolis in New York in Oakland. No more. The fear spent for a moment, for the smallest time fear of it passed. We dropped flower pots, dropped them like crazy old ladies on parades, only these were heavy mothers, heavy. Crack! Bang! Wham! There went a fuzz car roof. And another.

A few minutes later we ran down to South Field, past the barricades at the gates, the television lights, the whirling patrol car beacons, the policemen without badges, their helmets supporting plexiglass shields, the plainclothesmen in front of Furnald and Ferris Booth, everybody running around in near panic. Still the campus was free of the main body of uniformed police. They lined outside in great number near

157

the barricades on Amsterdam Avenue, in the side streets, waiting the word.

On South Field. Perhaps a thousand students gathered on the lawns and sidewalks before the library, near the sundial. I joined the crowd, losing Willie in the process. Rumors spread. The noise of shouting up near the Business School. Breaking glass. Two small fires started in Hamilton Hall, a larger fire in Fayerweather.

Andy and Philip came running up. "Come and help us," Philip said. I went off with them and near the barricades at Amsterdam we tried to pull paving stones from College Walk. It seemed very French, barricades, tearing up paving stones, very romantic. We got about eight pieces of paving from the sidewalk, but they were too bulky to carry and suddenly it seemed absurd. What in the hell would we use them for? Unable to decide, we hid them in the bushes near Hamilton Hall. Our stockpile. Our courage was back—we were doing something irrefutably revolutionary, doing something with our hands to protect ourselves—the October Days, Revolution pink and dawning, ineffably wonderful, hope in the tension ... and for some reason the phrase *Who is this who cometh from Edom with His garments red with blood?* kept running through my mind. A Cecil B. DeMille kick, Biblical, the Children of Israel or rather the Remnant after the Captivity facing now the sons of the Ten Lost Tribes, Gentiles, barbarians. I found myself imagining all the schmaltzy scenes from all the corny dramas and Hollywood French Revolution/Russian Revolution/Israel in Egypt-Land epics I had ever seen. I became an actor, depersonized, removed, invulnerable. It was a pageant. A show. No real pain or real blood. A spectacle. Cowboys and Indians at Guild rates. I was losing my mind. Through it before, yet it was unreal, a déja vu, some godawful mistake—the same show was being replayed, the same crummy parts, the same inevitability about the ending.

158

It was such incredibly bad casting, a B-film, second rate. Even the props were lousy.

About four o'clock tired, true Dean Alexander Platt—he remembered us—came out on his own, knowing the cops had been ordered to clear the campus (apparently Kirk had gotten on the campus station minutes before and told the students to get off campus or return to their rooms. The trouble was the radio played inside the buildings and most students were outside) and on his own initiative—for which he would pay— came to us and stood on the sundial and told us that his Eminence had ordered the pigs on to campus and everyone not under a dormitory bed would get his can kicked. Dean Platt. He was hurting inside. For us.

Philip and I (*Tis a far, far better thing I do*. Ronald Colman voice. Applause) ran to the Amsterdam gates and there, with about two hundred other losers, we locked arms and stood bravely before the barricades keeping the cops off our campus. *Ours*, friend. And standing with him I looked down the line to find Paul, remembering the doors before Math, for Paul. He wasn't there. He was over at Furnald getting his stomach kicked.

GODDAMN SMARTASS COMMIE PUNKS! Amen. Bursting through they came, the cops, tearing away our pathetic, ill-constructed barricades (at Math we had built the barricades thinking the doors opened in. They opened out. English majors. What do you expect?) pouring through like cows on a stampede. My courage broke, the fantasy slipped. Reality. I could feel my skin pressing, the scalp tingling in anticipation, my balls rising in the bag. Terror. I ran. Fast. Past the sundial and into the darkness of South Field.

Then I thought, the paving stones! Miles away. The cops arrested and beat the heroes and the slow-witted and the slow of foot at the gates. Philip among them. Will we never learn?

The cops moved on to campus. They formed a phalanx on College Walk from Broadway to Amsterdam, cutting the campus in two. There were over a thousand students back-walking before them down South Field toward Butler Library . . . Don't panic! running through my mind. Don't provoke. All I wanted was to get into Livingston out of trouble. Charlie Chicken-Hearted. I'd had it with the cops. The cop line broke and they started running after us. I remember the precise moment. No order was given that I could hear. But in the lights of College Walk, red lights and television light passing like airport beacons over their forms, suddenly their arms were raised, clubs high like Roman standards, badges hidden, and a sound, like a football team makes when it leaves the huddle and trundles hulking to the line, the sound a division of infantry—preferably Marines—makes as it rushes an enemy hill, that sound broke from them as they broke toward us. Girls screamed (in fact until dawn the campus was a fragmented chorus of people screaming) and some of us shouted—courage deflated, the heart giving up, but the mind, dazed, seconds behind—Motherfuckers! at the cops and ran. Many students fell, many were beaten, clubbed, stomped before they half neared the safety of the dorms. A couple ran to Ferris Booth chased by police and were pushed through the glass doors, the cops puffing and swinging behind. I ran toward the library and, with about twenty other students, circled around the tennis courts and entered the Van Am quad. Cops! Back we ran. Cops! Trapped. Then the body of us broke in different directions and the cops split in pursuit and most of us dived through the doors into Livingston.

It went on for hours. Every student in sight of a cop got clubbed. The police chased students into dorms and beat them in the lobbies and the halls, beat them before Ferris Booth (an infirmary established) and before Livingston (another infirmary). Police, with guns drawn, entered Furnald Hall and pulled boys from their rooms. Sweet New York Town.

I hid on the fifth floor of Livingston Hall (for about an

hour, to my lasting shame, I crouched in a stall in the john. And if I could have found an old lady's costume, dress, wig, falsies, friend, I would have put it on) absolutely piss-scared. But in time my curiosity got the best of my prudence and I went downstairs and snuck through the connecting lobbies into John Jay Hall. Looking through the window I watched a pack of plainclothesmen (the image that comes to my mind is a gang bang, a dockside rape, only foul and violently obscene) beat one girl and one boy with their fists, lining the two against the wall-base of the tennis court. One of the plainclothesmen wore a black-and-white flannel hunting shirt. Another wore a pea-green jacket that was zipped in the front. I watched a moment and left.

I ran back to Livingston and out into the quad. Serenity. The cops were not in sight. The students came out of buildings tentatively, cautiously at first, and then in larger numbers, bolder. They assembled by the round, temple-like monument in the center of the quad. We spoke in whispers. It was strange to stand there in a group in a hush while the noise of fighting elsewhere on campus came across the lawns to us.

Sophie came out of Hartley Hall and there was something about the atypical daintiness of her step, the slowness of it, that reminded me of Rachel. I missed her again and missing her I was grateful for Sophie's walk. Rachel. I went up to her. Her head was cut above the hairline and she held a handkerchief to the wound.

"Oh, Soph," I said, seeing the injury, "not you."

"The fuckers." That was all she said and then she pushed past me and crossed through the bushes on to South Field walking toward the groups of cops milling before Furnald.

About six o'clock I went into Livingston and up to Willie's room. I could not sleep. I sat by the window and watched the campus and skyline, the Hudson pushing into bay, the sun growing and shining gold off the windows of Furnald and

161

Journalism. There were cops everywhere in sight. The campus was vacant of everyone else. And except for an occasional student shouting an obscenity at the cops from a window it was quiet. I loved the place. Despite all that had happened, I loved Columbia. From where I sat I could look across toward the building where Professor Dodson had his office, I could see the window of Trilling's office. These men and us, that was what I loved. But I had not the heart for it that morning. Defiance was drained. I felt hollow and lonely, wanting peace. This bust was far worse than the first. Many more students injured much worse.

I went to sleep.

Later that day students told tales of beatings, of guns drawn, of brutality. They told what they had witnessed. Terror. Stunned. Nothing shocked me. Nothing drew response. Rage had seeped so low, filtered by guilt, spread around me, stinking from my pores, numbing me . . . rage was so complete (and necessary) a part of me that it was beyond degree. It was unvaried. Nothing could increase it. It was there. Me.

In the afternoon I went back to Willie's room. He was sitting on the lower bunk (Columbia's dormitory rooms are very small. Two bunk beds, two desks, a shelf and two chairs, a closet, a bare floor. Perhaps four feet of free space). He was naked except for a white towel lying across his thighs. Eighteen. He looked younger. His head bandaged. Seventeen stitches. His face distorted by huge welts and bruises. His right cheek bandaged. His chest cut, nail marks running from his right rib cage over to his left side under the nipple. The kid. Beaten.

Seeing my *friend* . . . love, anger, the compulsion to comfort and protect, the sense of protectlessness. I wanted to hold him and to kill the bastards who had harmed him. I wanted to kill.

"See," he said quietly, in the kind of monotone pain creates. "See," he said, standing up, his towel falling to the floor, the lock of uncut hair coming from under the bandage falling into the light ribboning his eyes. Blue. Far-country blue. Shaded in sunlight from the window. "See," he said, pointing to his groin to show me the welts and bruises near his sex, to his bruised legs, his V-ed back, wide and running narrowed, marked red, spoiled, the small of his back, his head bent toward me. I went to him and reached out hesitantly and touched his head and then gently felt his broken face with my finger, the cross marks from the blackjacks still embedded in his skin. My friend. And I remembered after the Liberation was broken a month before and his coming to his room in the afternoon and telling me laughingly that I needed a shower and our going together into the shower and bathing off the week of stench and dirt, and then playing under the water, snapping towels at each other, happy it was over and we were free, play-fighting under the water, being friends, and his standing outside on the tile floor, the light from the glazed window falling in a bent square at his feet, and wiping ourselves with towels and laughing because we were together after the Liberation, together and it had not been so bad and we had stood firm and right and had not disappointed each other, his standing on the cool floor, the light streaming white and gilding him (romantic, yes, but that is what it did, the water shining on his body like oil, the light gilding) and his eyes deeply blue in the light, his laughing and I see myself laughing with him in the mirror, laughing. He came from Canada, from some damn small farm town in Ontario, he came tough. What was it to him, this violent country? And now for me to stand before him unmarked, guilt-riddled, with his body aching with a beating, his face disfigured, his head cut open.

He told me how it happened. He was sitting in the lounge of Livingston Hall, kneeling on a chair facing the window.

This was after the first cop attack. A cop came by and he saw Willie and he hit him on the shoulder with his nightstick. The cop was wearing a helmet and a mask and no badge. "You cocksucker!" the cop said and started to climb into the window. Willie jumped down and turned and confronted six cops, badges hidden, standing behind him in the lounge. There, in the lobby of his dormitory, they beat him. Seven of them. *Big* men! Gutsy, All-American types! The lawanorder heads. They beat him with clubs and blackjacks and fists and boots. Lawanorder.

Later someone found him and took him to Saint Luke's Hospital and he was given a shot to dampen the pain and control the shock and then, waiting for stitches, he was put into a small room with a cop whose forehead was cut. This cop was with two plainclothesmen and Willie, bleeding, sat in the small room for nearly a half an hour and listened as the plainclothesmen and the cop called him a faggot and a fucker Commie and a college creep and told him how they would remember his face and get him again. Only they would kill the little Commie bastard next time. They told him they would remember.

Well, I will not forget.

the last chapter

SUMMER AGAIN. THE UNIVERSITY WAS TIRED, AS TIRED as the anti-war movement had become with Johnson's hint of peace talks, lifeless. I, too, was tired of politics and protest, tired of seeing my friends clubbed and beaten, tired of the American people and their violence and their war and their political shows and their unending spoilage of the poor land and the poorer people.

Summer again. Most of the members of the Columbia communes left town, Willie going to Canada to work, Brian to Long Island, Terry upstate, Philip to Philadelphia, Al to San Francisco. Those who remained turned their attention to the presidential campaign and to organizing for the Conventions. Time passed and we learned, with Robert Kennedy's death and with the Chicago Convention and with the Wallace candidacy, that the worst we had suspected about America was true. It was a depressing summer and fall.

I spent part of the summer sitting in on courses at Columbia, some of it on the Cape and out on Long Island, and some of it padding around the East Village where I met Rosalie—who reminded me in her despair and vulnerability, in the delicacy of her body, in her childlike need of Mission, of Rachel.

In the fall, as I got to know Rosalie and to love her in a

distant way—unpossessive, protective ot and responsive to what she caused me to remember—I began to reinvolve myself in the politics of disaffection, for she, being very young, was still made high by banging against the pigs.

In the late fall, George C. Wallace, Mr. Big with union labor, the country's most honest, most *American* politician, came into New York City. Rosalie and I went to confront him.

While I was outside Madison Square Garden playing street revolution with the cops, inside there were fifteen thousand fleshy, moist, screaming, patriotic types waiting for Wallace to come bounding on stage, his hands raised Nixonesque over his head, his smiles curled, his thin, deep eyes focusing around the auditorium looking for troublemakers. Wallace was in town to prove that nothing much had changed in New York since Charles Lindbergh regaled the America Firsters in the Old Garden and Gerald L. K. Smith and Father Coughlin, of the Shrine of Our Lady of the Little Flower, elevated hatred to faith, anti-Communism to infallible national doctrine, saying outloud what most Americans still believe, that this land and Holy Canaan Country are one in the same, folks, the Lost Ten Tribes making the wilderness bloom between the seas. Jesus Country. Of all the mad, incredibly, downright stupid religions Americans have invented (the list of charlatan bullshit is endless—from our native soil, friends, from our fear and conceit and incurable violence and inexpiable guilt, from the slaughters of red men and black men and white men and yellow men on this countryside, from our history denied, our deeds unadmitted, from our eyes lost in visions of Forever Progress, Science/Savior, from the knotty, torturous clit stump of our national remorse have come Mormonism, Christian Science, Russellism, I AMism, Scientology ... just to name a few) the ultimate blinder, the great, blood-red lying myth that gives pap to the Real America is, you guessed it, *Americanism*. Its high priest, Frightin' Judge Wallace from Alabama, traveling to tell us that New York City ("Jew York" as suburban rednecks west of the mighty Hudson term it) is in fact part of the good, ol' U.S. of A., put on the biggest, most charismatic, hate-mongering, thumping, patriotic esbat of the year. Mr. Popularity with American Labor, the seventh most admired man in the whole of this United States (a REPUBLIC, *not* a democracy, in case you forgot), preaching the gospel of the middle class—part Populist, part New Deal, part nationalistic, mostly sweet hate—in New York City of all places boggling the liberal mind. George Wallace. Not since Miss Aimee put on her Raise-High-The-Bloody-Flag-God-Bless-America-Ain't-Jesus-Good! stage shows at Los Angeles' Angeles Temple has the country seen a better political/religious showman. And, praise the Mercy of the Lord, the Judge, like the late, great, ever-popular Miss Aimee, is here to stay. He makes Nixon look like what Nixon is, a dull, drab, dank, dopey, duplicitous, dim dork. A white, hepatitic turd. Mr. Nixon. Inside the Garden, Wallace growled away as several thousand New Leftist antifascists acted out what has become a seasonal ritual—the politics of disaffection, of futility, the escalation of personal nihilism, the desire for dissolution.

We *need* George Wallace. After elections we still need the man. The Left does. After years of ambiguity he defines positions. He makes us true. Outside, a lady carrying a sign ("WALLACE + NIXON = HITLER + FRANCO") told me, "Wallace is going to lose the election and it's kind of bad. Really. Because he'd finally show us what we are. I hate his damn guts but the man's *honest*. Unlike Nixon or the others, the man's honest. You got to give him credit for that."

The lady's right. Wallace is as American as gumshoe cops and segregation and racist unions and Hubert Humphrey and lynchings and cherry pie and Rightwing assassinations. He *is*

Old Glory and Remember-The-Maine and Custer's Last Stand and Friday Night Bowling and Lyndon B. Johnson farting and glad-handing and beaming on the Texas ass-lickers at a bar-b-que at his ranch. He is the truest, the oldest, the most un-UnAmerican part of these fifty states. The Frontiersman. He IS America.

Eight-thirty at night. Cool, lovely night. I was running from the cops on 34th Street, in a crowd of a thousand antifascists on that particular New York street before the Garden, running fast after we called the cops pigs, motherfuckers, redneck bastards, you name it, sonsofbitches, and someone threw a bottle from the crowd and the cops went wild on their brown horses, swinging their clubs. . . . And as I was running from the police I thought of Rosalie. Lost her in the crowd somewhere an hour before in another cop chase before the Statler Hilton. I could not find her (she did not want me to. She did not *want me*).

That afternoon, knowing we would be taking to the street against Wallace, *that* afternoon she picked to tell me she was gone on chicks, hung on them, on *girls*, for Christ's sake! Girls, like they had better cocks or something. But that wasn't it, friend, it was that they had no hose shooting warm and life-filled, packing it, thundering trumpet, no God's Finger moving past the crazy, dizzy clit and through Its nail and cushion sending in the breath of life. No, friend, pricklessness sent her flying (but I also have dreamed of camping in a threesome with two lesbians, of being the unnecessary third, a prick an impediment like a stutter). Running I thought of Rosalie and I was glad she laid it on me. I *enjoyed* being told boys turned her off. If felt good in a hard sort of way, good like it feels when you provoke the cops, drive them up the goddamn wall with obscenities, and finally, with a kind of honest relief, they let go and start tearing after you. Schoolboys in a yard, the bully with the club. Very human then, that letting go, breaks the distance, passion and bias finally dropping from the gut into the street—the shield and uniform dissolve in the acid of a very human anger and they stand equal to you in the night. At last.

Rosalie was fifteen when I met her in August in the East Village, *east*, far east of Tompkins Park, living in a tenement filled with Puerto Rican junkies, and senile Jewesses abandoned by their families through death or indifference, trapped behind locked doors; and high school kids also trapped; Rosalie moving from one pad to another almost nightly, wall-to-wall mattresses, five, six runaways in a room, the boys outnumbering the girls two to one, refusing to admit to the constancy of their fear, hung between violence and morning, like mice nesting in their pads banishing the future and the past, fucking, shooting and sucking in the mary jane or worse after that perpetual high, elusive. Open. Too open. Rosalie. Pigtails, hell, like Margaret O'Brien used to wear. Gentle. Speaking in a small giggle. And each time I stayed with Rosalie (she wore loose pullovers, no bra or panties, sandals, one gold bracelet around her right wrist) I would sit naked on the bed—the mattress flat on the floor—at night, the air humid, hot, the windows boarded up to keep out the junkie thieves, usually several other couples in the room off somewhere on acid or pot or the still-new fuck, the room smelling in your mouth, tasted on the walls of your throat, smelling of bags of days' old garbage, cheap incense, grass burning, sweat, urine, wine, spilled beer, bad food . . . I would sit and Rosalie would very slowly lift her dress before me, take it off by gripping its shoulders and raising her hands high in the air, the cloth like a theatre curtain rising, revealing her thin calves, her knees—unwashed—her kid thighs, her sex, her hips, her little belly, the navel tiny and pink, and she would stand a moment giggling, her hands clutching the fabric stiff in the air, the material covering her head and breasts. I would sit and watch, aching to go on my knees, don't move, babe, not a muscle, not a hair, on my knees and began licking at her feet and up, up, round her world; staring, so hard-on it hurt, the head purple-red and glass-shiny, throbbing, ridiculous. For a night ... baby-sat ... and held her bringing to her what she considered *age* (My *God!* Twenty-six! Is that old?) and class (the smell of shaving lotion on a man and polished shoes—*class*) and held her, her body soft, flaxen, the pubic hair thin, light, lighter than her head, triangulated, young, strangely deprived of scent, each time I came away with guilt. My religious past, Holy Father. Guilt. Gave an edge to sex. As sin. Made it seem dirty (puritan mind) and corrupting. Leaving her, I had a desire for violence and humiliation. Like with some bull faggot truck driver on the docks. Or a mounted trooper on the street. Better still to find at long last the leitmotiv of the liberal sexual imagination: the massive, leathered, butch, delectably cruel German camp mistress ... can't you see her? Breasts bulging over leather bra (thick rawhide leather that gives off a straw/horse/stable odor, seeped in the smell of an ancient barn stall, the underside of a bull, the sweet/sour smell of a cow's udder), hip boots, wide belt, spread legs, the hair wild and long and coarse, the smell of wet copper and leather coming from the sweaty hollow of her thighs. Muscular. With a whip, naturally.

The afternoon of the Wallace rally I lay on the non-grass in Tompkins Park with Rosalie and the sun, hitting her face, the fuzz white, clean, reminding me of the smooth side of a boy's ass, I said, "Babe, you going nowhere in this scene. Nowhere, kid, and it'll kill you." Implacable virginity, feeling my age in the face of it, her wound closing each time, healing. Out of guilt I spoke, guilt she educed like a confessor.

"Where the hell am I to go?" she asked, sitting next to me,

170

glancing down at me, looking maddeningly innocent. "Where the hell am I supposed to go? There's no place *to* go!"

She was right. There was no place to go, unless she returned to her family upstate. And that was no place. But I was determined to get her off my back, I *had* to, for the town is so stuffed with lonely, vulnerable kids and they tie your heart with their weakness. What was I to do? I could not play Father/Lover to her expansive need forever. The heart is bounded.

At fifteen Rosalie was politically and sexually fucked up, increasingly the nation's sickness hers. More than twenty thousand young men had fled the country or the Armed Forces and she wondered why I stayed. Nearly thirty thousand dead in their war by November. Ten thousand jailed in American jails for political crimes. She wondered why I was free.

The week before, I had taken her up to Columbia where we joined an SDS demonstration that marched around campus and shouted: "Hey, hey, Cordier, how many blacks did you kill today?" Andrew Cordier, the new Acting President of Columbia University, former United Nations undersecretary, claimed by SDS to have been implicated in the killing of Congo premier Patrice Lumumba, Cordier alleged to be another CIA hack, which he, of course, denied. Is there anyone unbought? At night we marched over to a Columbia-owned tenement (the slum holes the University maintains for its neighbors and students) to protest the forced eviction of several aged indigents. The Pig Department was waiting. The protest got nowhere. But Rosalie started yelling, "Murdering pigs!" at the cops. She was pushed down, nearly clubbed. "For what?" I asked her, ticked at her imprudence, her thoughtless provocation, "for what did you yell that? Huh? It does no good, babe, no good."

She looked up at me, glaring her contempt. "You bastard! Why the hell don't you ever act like a man? Why the *hell* do you let those pigs get away with everything? Why?" She started to cry, frustrated, angered, impotent.

And later that week, heavy with war (I have learned to live with it, hating it) she got herself arrested downtown on Whitehall Street all alone sitting in the doorway of the SSS induction center, refusing to leave, protesting the draft, sitting there powerless while young men to be passed on to military camps were herded by her small body. I think she hated herself for being powerless (don't we all feel the guilt of our weakness?). I know she hated America.

"Why? You ask *me* why?" she said, angrily. I sat up and looked at her. She was off on a bitch. "What the fuck do *you* do, you aren't involved in the Columbia thing no more . . . ?" I started to protest, thinking that the two bloody busts on campus, the week in the commune, the months of strike work were certification enough, but she raised her hand to cut me off. ". . . I know you think Rudd's an ass and the Labor Committee [of SDS] is a bunch of middle-class idealists, but what the hell do you do, for shit! what do you do? *You?* How do *you* resist the war, you who always gives so damn much gutsy advice? Never in no public way, no way that'll get your ass in trouble. You sit on your butt, that's what you do, sit and bitch at me when I *try* to do something." It was an old argument. I read my lines.

"I don't think violent resistance, deliberate provocation, one or two people against a score of pigs, I don't think it makes any sense. It's not the time." I was lying. But I did not know what to do. I had tried just about all of it across the country and I had come to believe that my generation's response to and judgment on the use of violence was the central question of the age. And I had come to no conclusions.

"You're supposed to be the *man*, the one with the balls between the legs, yet you're the one always preaching moderation. *Moderation*," she repeated the word in a prissy faggot voice, "I'm tired of shitty moderation."

"You bitch!" I said, angered by her judgment. In my mind the phrase "the one with the balls" and the recollected image of her sweet mouth and tongue glazing my balls. Always she held me to some impossible standard, a romantic picture of manhood that I, at least, could never live up to. Me, because of *age* and *class*, she expected to be forever heavy-balled and strong. Well, I am worn of courage.

"Why don't you do something? Why do the girls always have to lead the way?"

My own fault. I had come to her boasting of a chain of Leftist triumphs—expanded with time, so fucking brave—that stretched from the Freedom Rides of the early Sixties through King's Washington March (Uncle Tom: "I have a dream!" Bang!) the U.N. bust, the nights at the Pentagon, the Columbia rebellion. Color me Red. And brave. Unadmitted my manhood, like so many other New Leftists, was tied intimately to the image of myself as nascent revolutionary. Rosalie refused to allow one to get by on intentions. She demanded *acts.* HISTORIC ACTS. I should go burning through the streets crying Babylon The Mighty Is Fallen! She wanted my martyrdom. A born widow. She wanted her very own lover's head to pomp around with. A pain in the ass. I tried to talk over her demand (there *were* Southern ambushes and KKK henchmen; there was Mississippi and Washington and Oakland and Chicago and Harlem). But how do you prove manhood once the question is publicly asked? Wear your sex exposed? Carry a gun? Nothing worked.

We changed the subject. Or at least I tried. Both of us stood and walked over to her pad. On the way she talked about Andy Warhol and his Superstars. Then she said, "I want to go to bed with N—— (one of his Superstars)."

"But she's a girl."

"I know, baby. That's why."

Deballed.

At seven o'clock that night she and I got off the subway at 34th Street and Eighth Avenue and joined the protest against Wallace in front of Madison Square Garden. I was upset (understatement) by what she had told me. And for the first time, after the scores of demonstrations I had been through, some of them bloody, it occurred to me that somehow in my America *my* manhood was profoundly connected with dissent. That in a country whose System emasculates young men, street disorders, seizures of buildings, dislocation, confrontation, the tempting of violence had become rituals of manhood.

We joined the crowd milling near Seventh Avenue. We moved from one block to another, trying to interpose ourselves between the Wallacites and the entrances to the Garden. At one point we surrounded a bus filled with Long Island crackers. We rocked it back and forth, threw stones and bottles at the windows, spit, shouted obscenities, and finally, before the police rescued the terrified passengers (their worst nightmares about the Communist-Zionist Conspiracy at the point of belief), smashed one of the windows. As we attacked the bus I do not think we cared anymore whether the demonstrations of the Left were self-defeating or not (Chicago had ended that consideration), whether they would in effect swing the country right or left. None of it mattered anymore, for none of us really believed in American democracy anymore. It was a fraud. No matter what we did or did not do, nothing would have a determining effect on the political system. We simply did not exist politically anymore. Demonstrations had become a kind of theatre, a play through which we mollified our outrage. We were doing what we had to do outside of political actuality. Violence was wanted. I hungered for it. I wanted to fight in front of my chick. To prove myself.

Rosalie got hurt in the first attack by the mounted police. The crowd was massed behind the barricades on the sidewalk.

Near the intersection one of the barricades gave way and suddenly we were all pushed through the wooden police fences by the pressure of the crowd behind us. Freedom, to run into the street stopping traffic, driving the foot police before us, for a moment taking control of one small area of the city. In America freedom is as rare and absurd as that.

There was a great deal of shouting—*two, four, six, eight, we don't want a fascist state*—and then the cop horsemen appeared rushing across the avenue into the crowd, trampling the demonstrators, driving small groups of people in the street on to the sidewalk and against the building, crushing those who could not escape. We all panicked. It was the common bust again, the Columbia terror, Chicago.

Rosalie and I ran up 34th Street. And then I looked to my side. She was gone. She had fallen. I saw her now behind the horses by the curb, on her knees in the street, her head down, her braids falling over her shoulders. At a distance she looked like a child and I remembered her age and vulnerability. I felt guilty. I wanted to run back, fighting my way through to the police and beyond to her, to protect her, hold her there in the street. And at the same time, I thought of her damn lesbian talk, her dyke confession. I hated her. I loved her. I hesitated and then I ran on, away from her.

I did not see her again that night. I went up to the West End Bar late at night and enjoyed my guilt. I did not look for her again that night. I did not look for her.

On Sunday night I went to the Theatre of the Ridiculous production of *The Moke-Eater* at Max's Kansas City bar. Its director, John Vaccaro, was an old friend of mine. Tally Brown was there (a Warhol queen, able to play both sides of the theatre scene, his epics *and* Broadway, slipping her fat body into *Mame* uptown) dressed in Pucci colors, reds, oranges, yellows, yards of thin, windblown material. She looked

175

like a moving wall of red gauze, her hair piled up like a fat Japanese dancer's, looking like nothing so much as a vast storm of butterfly wings gone mad. She eased herself into the seat next to me and *talked*, her inch-long false eyelashes fluttering, her tiny hands fluttering, her body fluttering, giving off the scent of some Oriental perfume, incense. She talked about what an absolute *genius* John Vaccaro was (that I already knew), how he and Ronnie Tavel had simply revolutionized American theatrical experience. "You know, darling, that he and Jack Smith and Andy [Warhol] are the three Pillars of Wisdom in the Underground, the Triumvirate?" No, that I didn't know.

Rich Lorber, a young writer and a Columbia friend of mine (he wrote a book called *The Gap*), sat on the other side of me, dead sober, lost on a girl lost to him now, missing love. The room filled quickly. Then, while the lights dimmed, in came Jackie Curtis and Candy Darling, two of Warhol's Superstars. Jackie, playing Audrey Hepburn, was dressed in a long, black velvet cloak, lightly madeup face, short, sandy-colored hair, demure, femme. And Candy Darling. A beauty in the semi-darkness, platinum hair flowing and loose like Marilyn Monroe's, a tight black sheath, comfortable breasts, a rhinestone bracelet. And the air of a queen, mysterious, silent, exuding the aura of Marlene—I have been everywhere, seen everything, done it all; nothing seizes me but boredom.

The play began. Bruce Pecheur, a $2000-a-week model Vaccaro had enticed into the company, came on stage playing Jack/Fred, the moke, the dolt, the unbearable, unteachable straight (Bruce in life is uptight, straight. A Harvard graduate with a pretty face, bright, hoping to replace Rock Hudson in Doris Day's future bed. When he came months before to Vaccaro's loft to try out for the part, Vaccaro had the cast rush at him and strip him). The play was one long, painful ritual of humiliation and aggression. By the end, Jack/Fred had been breastfed, peed on stage, fucked, eaten, and finally disemboweled. Ritual murder. Why We Are In Vietnam, as Mailer would say, staged above a bar.

I sat in the row behind Jackie and Candy Darling and watched as Candy sat immobile, unimpressed, the ennui of the race settled on her delicate face. She was tiny like Rosalie, like Rachel. And watching her from the rear, her hands occasionally lifted to her mouth to hide a laugh or gasp, occasionally fluffing her white-blonde hair, feminine, watching her I was impressed by her sexual immaculateness. She was like a toy or doll to be viewed and touched but never entered. Never known. I thought of how Hemingway was beguiled for decades by Marlene, he moving into age and desperation while she remained unchanged, forever teasing, just a hint of corruption beneath a virgin beauty. Marlene/Candy Darling.

After the play Lorber and I went to a party some of the cast was giving. It was a wild affair. Tally sitting enthroned in a chair before a round table. Vaccaro, Pecheur, several others sitting around it smoking and laughing. Candy Darling and Jackie Curtis languid on the bed in the back room, giving passing guests their come-hither looks, playing it as femme and Superstar as they could, reducing us to fans, tender numbers with a glance. Candy, still-life, brushed by sadness.

I drank. Heavily. I wanted a lesbian that night. Not Rosalie, but simply some lesbian to see what it felt like (a high school attitude—to see what it felt like). The guests talked about the Wallace meeting and the street disorders, about the situation at Columbia, about the theatre, about themselves and their Careers. This was their Hollywood party in Little Italy, as much of Hollywood as they would know, Vaccaro their Cecil B. DeMille, Jackie/Hepburn, Candy/ Marlene, Tally the Established Box Office Star, Lorber and I the Trade Writers, Pecheur/Rock Hudson, and the others acted as starlets and directors and angels. It was a farce from the beginning to the end, a continuation of the play itself. No one had changed costumes. Or roles. Life was artifice. Death fantasy.

I went into the back room where Candy Darling and Jackie and the other painted dolls held court. They huddled in little groups—Candy the silent, mysterious center—and gossiped excitedly about feeling Joe Dallesandro in *Flesh* (Warhol's newest film, his newest discovery at the time and his most handsome), eyelashes a mile out and blinking frantically, the Queen's Night Parade, women at last, at last, Dear God! and I thought of Rosalie off somewhere with her new dyke husband, missing me (?) and I, fatigued by politics without power, wanting what? Obliteration? And blinking they babbled about Columbia (how goddamn *masculine* I felt alone with the girls, all but Candy Darling I thought inauthentic, queens who became Queens at six), asking me if the revolt would go on, the weight of their heavy anguish, brokenness, unspeakable loss, resting in our pretended triumph. Had THEY worn us through? Motherfuckers, had they broken us? And I, would I who had not marched *for* anything since June, who no longer believed, tell them that fall their hope was false? I boasted. I strutted. I spoke easily of revolution in America, falling into the role of Rebel. And Candy Darling sitting wide-eyed on the bed, full of wonderment over *me*, setting me off, sexy, Christ, with her Marilyn hair and small nose and youth (Rosalie!). I strutted. I talked about the Wallace demonstration, enlarged my role, revised the scene to cut Rosalie out, restored my manhood.

I had another drink. I pulled Candy on to a corner of the bed. I came on like a horny truck driver. She blinked, fluttered, played the Virgin. And she asked, of all things, "Do you know Gore Vidal?"

What the hell could I say? I lied. "Good friend of mine." Never met the man in my life.

"Oh, that's marvelous!" she gushed, in a heavy, throaty voice. "I want to play Myra Breckinridge. So *bad*. Do you suppose..." the virgin opening for a promise, "do you suppose you could introduce him to me, Dotson?"

In the afternoon two days later I saw Girard Malanga at a party. I told him about Candy Darling, how wild I was about her.

"But she's a boy," he said.

In three weeks I saw Rosalie again at a distance in the Barnard gym at an SDS meeting, with a bull dyke, both of them dressed in army fatigues. Above her right cheek was a dark bruise. I loved her. Confusing, the center would not hold. The two girl lovers. It didn't make any sense. Nothing did. Somehow my life had degenerated into a series of losses, of a lack of fulfillment, of gestures of violence.

For us America was a divided country facing civil war. Fighting had already begun as early as 1964 and I had been part of some of its earliest skirmishes. It was divided between the victims and the authorities and I found myself irrevocably on the weaker side because, quite simply, that was the country of my friends. And I knew—and this was the only meaningful experience—that the only community any of us would know was the community of the victims. For we were cut off, all of us, from what Dick Nixon likes to call the "mainstream of American life." We were apart. We were the young and black and radical and disaffected and the homosexual and the head. We were the Non-believers. Our failure was the fact that we continually sought community apart from ourselves, reprieving daily the American Dream that was sold to us long ago, unable to concede that the only possible community was in rebellion. And it was not simply political victimhood, but the pain of being outside—sometime go in the winter in the

East Village or hippie colonies in other cities and witness the pain—and it evidenced itself in our art and sex and learning and life style. If Eldridge Cleaver was correct when he said that a civil war could be fought between one dissenter and his nation, then a civil war was going on in America.